www.EffortlessMath.com

... So Much More Online!

✓ FREE Math lessons

✓ More Math learning books!

✓ Mathematics Worksheets

✓ Online Math Tutors

Need a PDF version of this book?

Send email to: Info@EffortlessMath.com

Prepare for the DAT Quantitative Reasoning Test in 7 Days

A Quick Study Guide with Two Full-Length DAT

Quantitative Reasoning Practice Tests

By

Reza Nazari & Ava Ross

All inquiries should be addressed to:

info@effortlessMath.com

www.EffortlessMath.com

ISBN–13: 978-1-64612-133-5

ISBN–10: 1-64612-133-3

Published by: Effortless Math Education

www.EffortlessMath.com

Description

Prepare for the DAT Quantitative Reasoning Test in 7 Days, which reflects the 2019 and 2020 test guidelines and topics, incorporates the best method and the right strategies to help you hone your math skills, overcome your exam anxiety, and boost your confidence -- and do your best to defeat DAT Quantitative Reasoning test quickly. This quick study guide contains only the most important and critical math concepts a student will need in order to succeed on the DAT Quantitative Reasoning test. Math concepts in this book break down the topics, so the material can be quickly grasped. Examples are worked step–by–step to help you learn exactly what to do.

This DAT Quantitative Reasoning new edition has been updated to duplicate questions appearing on the most recent DAT Quantitative Reasoning tests. It contains easy–to–read essential summaries that highlight the key areas of the DAT Quantitative Reasoning test. You only need to spend about 3 – 5 hours daily in your 7–day period in order to achieve your goal. After reviewing this book, you will have solid foundation and adequate practice that is necessary to fully prepare for the DAT Quantitative Reasoning.

Prepare for the DAT Quantitative Reasoning Test in 7 Days is for all DAT test takers. It is a breakthrough in Math learning — offering a winning formula and the most powerful methods for learning basic Math topics confidently. Each section offers step–by–step instruction and helpful hints, with a few topics being tackled each day.

Inside the pages of this comprehensive book, students can learn math topics in a structured manner with a complete study program to help them understand essential math skills. It also has many exciting features, including:

- Content 100% aligned with the 2019-2020 DAT test
- Written by DAT Quantitative Reasoning tutors and test experts
- Complete coverage of all DAT Quantitative Reasoning concepts and topics which you will be tested
- Step-by-step guide for all DAT Quantitative Reasoning topics
- Dynamic design and easy-to-follow activities
- Over 600 additional DAT Quantitative Reasoning practice questions in both multiple-choice and grid-in formats with answers grouped by topic, so you can focus on your weak areas
- 2 full-length practice tests (featuring new question types) with detailed answers

Effortlessly and confidently follow the step–by–step instructions in this book to prepare for the DAT Quantitative Reasoning in a short period of time.

Prepare for the DAT Quantitative Reasoning Test in 7 Days is the only book you'll ever need to master Basic Math topics! It can be used as a self–study course – you do not need to work with a Math tutor. (It can also be used with a Math tutor).

Ideal for self–study as well as for classroom usage.

About the Author

Reza Nazari is the author of more than 100 Math learning books including:
– **Math and Critical Thinking Challenges:** For the Middle and High School Student
– **GRE Math in 30 Days**
– **ASVAB Math Workbook 2018 - 2019**
– **Effortless Math Education Workbooks**
– **and many more Mathematics books ...**

Reza is also an experienced Math instructor and a test–prep expert who has been tutoring students since 2008. Reza is the founder of Effortless Math Education, a tutoring company that has helped many students raise their standardized test scores—and attend the colleges of their dreams. Reza provides an individualized custom learning plan and the personalized attention that makes a difference in how students view math.

You can contact Reza via email at:
reza@EffortlessMath.com

Find Reza's professional profile at:
goo.gl/zoC9rJ

Contents

Day 1:
Fundamental and Building Blocks

Math Topics that you'll learn today:

- ✓ Simplifying Fractions
- ✓ Adding and Subtracting Fractions
- ✓ Multiplying and Dividing Fractions
- ✓ Adding Mixed Numbers
- ✓ Subtracting Mixed Numbers
- ✓ Multiplying Mixed Numbers
- ✓ Dividing Mixed Numbers
- ✓ Rounding Decimals
- ✓ Adding and Subtracting Decimals
- ✓ Multiplying and Dividing Decimals

"A Man is like a fraction whose numerator is what he is and whose denominator is what he thinks of himself.
The larger the denominator, the smaller the fraction." -Tolstoy

Simplifying Fractions

Step-by-step guide:

- ✓ Evenly divide both the top and bottom of the fraction by $2, 3, 5, 7, \dots$ etc.

- ✓ Continue until you can't go any further.

Examples:

1) Simplify $\frac{12}{20}$. To simplify $\frac{12}{20}$, find a number that both 12 and 20 are divisible by. Both are divisible by 4. Then: $\frac{12}{20} = \frac{12 \div 4}{20 \div 4} = \frac{3}{5}$

2) Simplify $\frac{64}{80}$. To simplify $\frac{64}{80}$, find a number that both 64 and 80 are divisible by. Both are divisible by 8 and 16. Then: $\frac{64}{80} = \frac{64 \div 8}{80 \div 8} = \frac{8}{10}$, 8 and 10 are divisible by 2, then: $\frac{8}{10} = \frac{4}{5}$
or $\frac{64}{80} = \frac{64 \div 16}{80 \div 16} = \frac{4}{5}$

Adding and Subtracting Fractions

Step-by-step guide:

- ✓ For "like" fractions (fractions with the same denominator), add or subtract the numerators and write the answer over the common denominator.

- ✓ Find equivalent fractions with the same denominator before you can add or subtract fractions with different denominators.

- ✓ Adding and Subtracting with the same denominator:

$$\frac{a}{b} + \frac{c}{b} = \frac{a+c}{b} \ , \frac{a}{b} - \frac{c}{b} = \frac{a-c}{b}$$

- ✓ Adding and Subtracting fractions with different denominators:

$$\frac{a}{b} + \frac{c}{d} = \frac{ad+c}{bd} \ , \frac{a}{b} - \frac{c}{d} = \frac{ad-cb}{bd}$$

Examples:

1) Calculate. $\frac{4}{5} - \frac{3}{5} =$

   For "like" fractions, subtract the numerators and write the answer over the common denominator. Then: $\frac{4}{5} - \frac{3}{5} = \frac{1}{5}$

2) Subtract fractions. $\frac{2}{3} - \frac{1}{2} =$

   For "unlike" fractions, find equivalent fractions with the same denominator before you can add or subtract fractions with different denominators. Use this formula: $\frac{a}{b} - \frac{c}{d} = \frac{ad - cb}{bd}$

   $\frac{2}{3} - \frac{1}{2} = \frac{(2)(2) - (1)(3)}{3 \times 2} = \frac{4-3}{6} = \frac{1}{6}$

Multiplying and Dividing Fractions

Step-by-step guide:

- ✓ Multiplying fractions: multiply the top numbers and multiply the bottom numbers.

- ✓ Dividing fractions: Keep, Change, Flip

- ✓ Keep first fraction, change division sign to multiplication, and flip the numerator and denominator of the second fraction. Then, solve!

Examples:

1) Multiplying fractions. $\frac{5}{6} \times \frac{3}{4} =$

   Multiply the top numbers and multiply the bottom numbers.

   $\frac{5}{6} \times \frac{3}{4} = \frac{5 \times 3}{6 \times 4} = \frac{15}{24}$, simplify: $\frac{15}{24} = \frac{15 \div 3}{24 \div 3} = \frac{5}{8}$

2) Dividing fractions. $\frac{1}{4} \div \frac{2}{3} =$

   Keep first fraction, change division sign to multiplication, and flip the numerator and denominator of the second fraction. Then: $\frac{1}{4} \times \frac{3}{2} = \frac{1 \times 3}{4 \times 2} = \frac{3}{8}$

Adding Mixed Numbers

Step-by-step guide:

Use the following steps for both adding and subtracting mixed numbers.

- ✓ Add whole numbers of the mixed numbers.
- ✓ Add the fractions of each mixed number.
- ✓ Find the Least Common Denominator (LCD) if necessary.
- ✓ Add whole numbers and fractions.
- ✓ Write your answer in lowest terms.

Examples:

1) Add mixed numbers. $1\frac{3}{4} + 2\frac{3}{8} =$

Rewriting our equation with parts separated, $1 + \frac{3}{4} + 2 + \frac{3}{8}$, Solving the whole number parts $1 + 2 = 3$, Solving the fraction parts $\frac{3}{4} + \frac{3}{8}$, and rewrite to solve with the equivalent fractions.

$\frac{6}{8} + \frac{3}{8} = \frac{9}{8} = 1\frac{1}{8}$, then Combining the whole and fraction parts $3 + 1 + \frac{1}{8} = 4\frac{1}{8}$

2) Add mixed numbers. $1\frac{2}{3} + 4\frac{1}{6} =$

Rewriting our equation with parts separated, $1 + \frac{2}{3} + 4 + \frac{1}{6}$, Solving the whole number parts $1 + 4 = 5$, Solving the fraction parts $\frac{2}{3} + \frac{1}{6}$, and rewrite to solve with the equivalent fractions.

$\frac{2}{3} + \frac{1}{6} = \frac{5}{6}$, then Combining the whole and fraction parts $5 + \frac{5}{6} = 5\frac{5}{6}$

Subtracting Mixed Numbers

Step-by-step guide:

Use the following steps for both adding and subtracting mixed numbers.

- ✓ Subtract the whole number of second mixed number from whole number of the first mixed number.
- ✓ Subtract the second fraction from the first one.
- ✓ Find the Least Common Denominator (LCD) if necessary.
- ✓ Add the result of whole numbers and fractions.
- ✓ Write your answer in lowest terms.

Examples:

1) Subtract. $5\frac{2}{3} - 2\frac{1}{4} =$

Rewriting our equation with parts separated, $5 + \frac{2}{3} - 2 - \frac{1}{4}$

Solving the whole number parts $5 - 2 = 3$, Solving the fraction parts, $\frac{2}{3} - \frac{1}{4} = \frac{8-3}{12} = \frac{5}{12}$

Combining the whole and fraction parts, $3 + \frac{5}{12} = 3\frac{5}{12}$

2) Subtract. $3\frac{4}{5} - 1\frac{1}{2} =$

Rewriting our equation with parts separated, $3 + \frac{4}{5} - 1 - \frac{1}{2}$

Solving the whole number parts $3 - 1 = 2$, Solving the fraction parts, $\frac{4}{5} - \frac{1}{2} = \frac{3}{10}$

Combining the whole and fraction parts, $2 + \frac{3}{10} = 2\frac{3}{10}$

Multiplying Mixed Numbers

Step-by-step guide:

- ✓ Convert the mixed numbers to improper fractions. (improper fraction is a fraction in which the top number is bigger than bottom number)
- ✓ Multiply fractions and simplify if necessary. $a\frac{c}{b} = a + \frac{c}{b} = \frac{ab+c}{b}$

Examples:

1) Multiply mixed numbers. $3\frac{2}{3} \times 2\frac{1}{2} =$

Converting mixed numbers to fractions, $3\frac{2}{3} = \frac{11}{3}$ and $2\frac{1}{2} = \frac{5}{2}$.

$\frac{11}{3} \times \frac{5}{2}$, Applying the fractions formula for multiplication, $\frac{11\times5}{3\times2} = \frac{55}{6} = 9\frac{1}{6}$

2) Multiply mixed numbers. $4\frac{3}{5} \times 2\frac{1}{3} =$

Converting mixed numbers to fractions, $\frac{23}{5} \times \frac{7}{3}$, Applying the fractions formula for multiplication, $\frac{23\times7}{5\times3} = \frac{161}{15} = 10\frac{11}{15}$

Dividing Mixed Numbers

Step-by-step guide:

- ✓ Convert the mixed numbers to improper fractions.
- ✓ Divide fractions and simplify if necessary.

$$a\frac{c}{b} = a + \frac{c}{b} = \frac{ab+c}{b}$$

Examples:

1) Find the quotient. $2\frac{1}{2} \div 1\frac{1}{5} =$

Converting mixed numbers to fractions, $\frac{5}{2} \div \frac{6}{5}$, Applying the fractions formula for multiplication, $\frac{5\times5}{2\times6} = \frac{25}{12} = 2\frac{1}{12}$

2) Find the quotient. $4\frac{3}{4} \div 3\frac{4}{5} =$

Converting mixed numbers to fractions, $\frac{19}{4} \div \frac{19}{5}$, Applying the fractions formula for multiplication, $\frac{19\times5}{4\times19} = \frac{95}{76} = 1\frac{1}{4}$

Rounding Decimals

Step-by-step guide:

- ✓ We can round decimals to a certain accuracy or number of decimal places. This is used to make calculation easier to do and results easier to understand, when exact values are not too important.
- ✓ First, you'll need to remember your place values: For example:

12. 4567

1: tens	2: ones	4: tenths
5: hundredths	6: thousandths	7: tens thousandths

- ✓ To round a decimal, find the place value you'll round to.
- ✓ Find the digit to the right of the place value you're rounding to. If it is 5 or bigger, add 1 to the place value you're rounding to and remove all digits on its right side. If the digit to the right of the place value is less than 5, keep the place value and remove all digits on the right.

Examples:

1) Round 2.1837 to the thousandth place value.

First look at the next place value to the right, (tens thousandths). It's 7 and it is greater than 5. Thus add 1 to the digit in the thousandth place.

Thousandth place is 3. $\rightarrow 3 + 1 = 4$, then, the answer is 2.184

2) 2.1837 rounded to the nearest hundredth.

First look at the next place value to the right of thousandths. It's 3 and it is less than 5, thus remove all the digits to the right. Then, the answer is 2.18.

Adding and Subtracting Decimals

Step-by-step guide:

✓ Line up the numbers.

✓ Add zeros to have same number of digits for both numbers if necessary.

✓ Add or subtract using column addition or subtraction.

Examples:

1) Add. $2.5 + 1.24 =$

First line up the numbers: $\begin{array}{r} 2.5 \\ + 1.24 \\ \hline \end{array}$ $\rightarrow$ Add zeros to have same number of digits for both

numbers. $\begin{array}{r} 2.50 \\ + 1.24 \\ \hline \end{array}$, Start with the hundredths place. $0 + 4 = 4$, $\begin{array}{r} 2.50 \\ + 1.24 \\ \hline 4 \end{array}$, Continue with tenths

place. $5 + 2 = 7$, $\begin{array}{r} 2.50 \\ + 1.24 \\ \hline .74 \end{array}$. Add the ones place. $2 + 1 = 3$, $\begin{array}{r} 2.50 \\ + 1.24 \\ \hline 3.74 \end{array}$

2) Subtract decimals. $4.67 - 2.15 =$ $\begin{array}{r} 4.67 \\ - 2.15 \\ \hline \end{array}$

Start with the hundredths place. $7 - 5 = 2$, $\begin{array}{r} 4.67 \\ - 2.15 \\ \hline 2 \end{array}$, continue with tenths place. $6 - 1 = 5$

$\begin{array}{r} 4.67 \\ - 2.15 \\ \hline .52 \end{array}$, subtract the ones place. $4 - 2 = 2$, $\begin{array}{r} 4.67 \\ - 2.15 \\ \hline 2.52 \end{array}$.

Multiplying and Dividing Decimals

Step-by-step guide:

For Multiplication:

✓ Ignore the decimal point and set up and multiply the numbers as you do with whole numbers.
Count the total number of decimal places in both of the factors.
Place the decimal point in the product.
For Division:

✓ If the divisor is not a whole number, move decimal point to right to make it a whole number. Do the same for dividend.
✓ Divide similar to whole numbers.

Examples:

1) Find the product. $0.50 \times 0.20 =$

Set up and multiply the numbers as you do with whole numbers. Line up the numbers: $\begin{array}{r} 50 \\ \times\, 20 \\ \hline \end{array}$, Start with the ones place → $50 \times 0 = 0$, $\begin{array}{r} 50 \\ \times 20 \\ \hline 0 \end{array}$, Continue with other digits → $50 \times 2 = 100$, $\begin{array}{r} 50 \\ \times 20 \\ \hline 1,000 \end{array}$, Count the total number of decimal places in both of the factors. (4). Then Place the decimal point in the product.

Then: $\begin{array}{r} 0.50 \\ \times\, 0.20 \\ \hline 0.1000 \end{array}$ → $0.50 \times 0.20 = 0.1$

2) Find the quotient. $1.20 \div 0.2 =$

The divisor is not a whole number. Multiply it by 10 to get 2. Do the same for the dividend to get 12. Now, divide: $12 \div 2 = 6$. The answer is 6.

Day 1 Practices

✍ *Simplify each fraction.*

1) $\dfrac{27}{54} =$

2) $\dfrac{48}{60} =$

3) $\dfrac{42}{56} =$

4) $\dfrac{30}{120} =$

5) $\dfrac{36}{48} =$

6) $\dfrac{18}{27} =$

✍ *Find the sum or difference.*

7) $\dfrac{12}{19} + \dfrac{7}{19} =$

8) $\dfrac{2}{4} + \dfrac{3}{9} =$

9) $\dfrac{3}{5} + \dfrac{2}{3} =$

10) $\dfrac{3}{7} + \dfrac{2}{3} =$

11) $\dfrac{1}{2} - \dfrac{1}{3} =$

12) $\dfrac{8}{10} - \dfrac{4}{6} =$

✍ *Find the answers.*

13) $\dfrac{3}{6} \times \dfrac{6}{8} =$

14) $\dfrac{1}{5} \times \dfrac{1}{3} =$

15) $\dfrac{1}{4} \times \dfrac{2}{5} =$

16) $\dfrac{1}{6} \times \dfrac{4}{5} =$

17) $\dfrac{1}{5} \times \dfrac{1}{4} =$

18) $\dfrac{2}{5} \times \dfrac{1}{2} =$

✍ *Calculate.*

19) $5\dfrac{1}{2} + 2\dfrac{1}{3} =$

20) $8\dfrac{1}{2} - 3\dfrac{1}{2} =$

21) $5\dfrac{3}{8} + 3\dfrac{1}{8} =$

22) $6\dfrac{1}{2} - 3\dfrac{1}{4} =$

23) $1\dfrac{3}{7} - 1\dfrac{3}{14} =$

24) $7\dfrac{5}{12} + 2\dfrac{3}{4} =$

✎ **Find the answers.**

25) $4\frac{1}{3} \times 2\frac{1}{5} =$

27) $5\frac{2}{5} \div 2\frac{1}{3} =$

29) $3\frac{4}{7} \div 2\frac{3}{5} =$

26) $3\frac{1}{2} \times 3\frac{1}{4} =$

28) $2\frac{1}{2} \times 1\frac{2}{9} =$

30) $7\frac{2}{3} \div 2\frac{2}{3} =$

✎ **Round each decimal to the nearest whole number.**

31) 23.48

33) 14.47

35) 3.92

32) 8.7

34) 7.5

36) 56.8

✎ **Find the sum or difference.**

37) $34.13 - 14.45 =$

39) $75.50 + 20.78 =$

41) $73.47 + 14.25 =$

38) $37.25 + 22.47 =$

40) $58.67 - 46.39 =$

42) $69.99 - 54.61 =$

✎ **Find the product and quotient.**

43) $0.6 \times 0.3 =$

45) $1.25 \times 0.5 =$

47) $1.92 \times 0.8 =$

44) $4.6 \div 0.2 =$

46) $0.72 \div 0.2 =$

48) $0.52 \div 0.4 =$

Answers

1) $\frac{1}{2}$

2) $\frac{4}{5}$

3) $\frac{3}{4}$

4) $\frac{1}{4}$

5) $\frac{3}{4}$

6) $\frac{2}{3}$

7) $\frac{19}{19} = 1$

8) $\frac{5}{6}$

9) $\frac{19}{15}$

10) $\frac{23}{21}$

11) $\frac{1}{6}$

12) $\frac{2}{15}$

13) $\frac{3}{8}$

14) $\frac{1}{15}$

15) $\frac{1}{10}$

16) $\frac{2}{15}$

17) $\frac{1}{20}$

18) $\frac{1}{5}$

19) $7\frac{5}{6}$

20) 5

21) $8\frac{1}{2}$

22) $3\frac{1}{4}$

23) $\frac{3}{14}$

24) $10\frac{1}{6}$

25) $9\frac{8}{15}$

26) $11\frac{3}{8}$

27) $2\frac{11}{35}$

28) $3\frac{1}{18}$

29) $1\frac{34}{91}$

30) $2\frac{7}{8}$

31) 23

32) 9

33) 14

34) 8

35) 4

36) 57

37) 19.68

38) 59.72

39) 96.28

40) 12.28

41) 87.72

42) 15.38

43) 0.18

44) 23

45) 0.625

46) 3.6

47) 1.536

48) 1.3

Day 2:
Integers, Ratios, and Proportions

Math Topics that you'll learn today:

- ✓ Adding and Subtracting Integers
- ✓ Multiplying and Dividing Integers
- ✓ Ordering Integers and Numbers
- ✓ Order of Operations
- ✓ Integers and Absolute Value
- ✓ Simplifying Ratios
- ✓ Proportional Ratios
- ✓ Create a Proportion
- ✓ Similarity and Ratios

Without mathematics, there's nothing you can do. Everything around you is mathematics. Everything around you is numbers." - Shakuntala Devi

Adding and Subtracting Integers

Step-by-step guide:

- ✓ Integers includes: zero, counting numbers, and the negative of the counting numbers. $\{\ldots, -3, -2, -1, 0, 1, 2, 3, \ldots\}$
- ✓ Add a positive integer by moving to the right on the number line.
- ✓ Add a negative integer by moving to the left on the number line.
- ✓ Subtract an integer by adding its opposite.

Examples:

1) Solve. $(-8) - (-5) =$

Keep the first number and convert the sign of the second number to its opposite. (change subtraction into addition. Then: $(-8) + 5 = -3$

2) Solve. $10 + (4 - 8) =$

First subtract the numbers in brackets, $4 - 8 = -4$

Then: $10 + (-4) = \rightarrow$ change addition into subtraction: $10 - 4 = 6$

Multiplying and Dividing Integers

Step-by-step guide:

Use these rules for multiplying and dividing integers:

- ✓ (negative) × (negative) = positive
- ✓ (negative) ÷ (negative) = positive
- ✓ (negative) × (positive) = negative
- ✓ (negative) ÷ (positive) = negative
- ✓ (positive) × (positive) = positive

Examples:

1) Solve. $(2 - 5) \times (3) =$

First subtract the numbers in brackets, $2 - 5 = -3 \rightarrow (-3) \times (3) =$

Now use this formula: (negative) × (positive) = negative
$(-3) \times (3) = -9$

2) Solve. $(-12) + (48 \div 6) =$

First divided 48 by 6 , the numbers in brackets, $48 \div 6 = 8$

$= (-12) + (8) = -12 + 8 = -4$

Ordering Integers and Numbers

Step-by-step guide:

- ✓ When using a number line, numbers increase as you move to the right.
- ✓ When comparing two numbers, think about their position on number line. If one number is on the right side of another number, it is a bigger number. For example, -3 is bigger than -5 because it is on the right side of -5 on number line.

Examples:

1) Order this set of integers from least to greatest. $-2, 1, -5, -1, 2, 4$
The smallest number is -5 and the largest number is 4.

Now compare the integers and order them from greatest to least:
$-5 < -2 < -1 < 1 < 2 < 4$

2) Order each set of integers from greatest to least. $10, -6, -2, 5, -8, 4$
The largest number is 10 and the smallest number is -8.

Now compare the integers and order them from least to greatest:
$10 > 5 > 4 > -2 > -6 > -8$

Order of Operations

Step-by-step guide:

When there is more than one math operation, use PEMDAS:

✓ Parentheses

✓ Exponents

✓ Multiplication and Division (from left to right)

✓ Addition and Subtraction (from left to right)

Examples:

1) Solve. $(5 + 7) \div (3^2 \div 3) =$

First simplify inside parentheses: $(12) \div (9 \div 3) = (12) \div (3) =$
Then: $(12) \div (3) = 4$

2) Solve. $(11 \times 5) - (12 - 7) =$

First simplify inside parentheses: $(11 \times 5) - (12 - 7) = (55) - (5) =$

Then: $(55) - (5) = 50$

Integers and Absolute Value

Step-by-step guide:

✓ To find an absolute value of a number, just find its distance from 0 on number line! For example, the distance of 12 and -12 from zero on number line is 12!

Examples:

1) Solve. $\frac{|-18|}{9} \times |5 - 8| =$

First find $|-18|$, →the absolute value of -18 is 18, then: $|-18| = 18$
$\frac{18}{9} \times |5 - 8| =$
Next, solve $|5 - 8|$, → $|5 - 8| = |-3|$, the absolute value of -3 is 3. $|-3| = 3$

Then: $\frac{18}{9} \times 3 = 2 \times 3 = 6$

2) Solve. $|10 - 5| \times \frac{|-2 \times 6|}{3} =$

First solve $|10 - 5|$, $\rightarrow |10 - 5| = |5|$, the absolute value of 5 is 5, $|5| = 5$

$5 \times \frac{|-2 \times 6|}{3} =$

Now solve $|-2 \times 6|$, $\rightarrow |-2 \times 6| = |-12|$, the absolute value of -12 is 12, $|-12| = 12$

Then: $5 \times \frac{12}{3} = 5 \times 4 = 20$

Simplifying Ratios

Step-by-step guide:

- ✓ Ratios are used to make comparisons between two numbers.
- ✓ Ratios can be written as a fraction, using the word "to", or with a colon.
- ✓ You can calculate equivalent ratios by multiplying or dividing both sides of the ratio by the same number.

Examples:

1) Simplify. $8 : 4 =$

Both numbers 8 and 4 are divisible by 4 , $\Rightarrow 8 \div 4 = 2, 4 \div 4 = 1$,

Then: $8 : 4 = 2 : 1$

2) Simplify. $\frac{12}{36} =$

Both numbers 12 and 36 are divisible by 12, $\Rightarrow 12 \div 12 = 1, 36 \div 12 = 3$,

Then: $\frac{12}{36} = \frac{1}{3}$

Proportional Ratios

Step-by-step guide:

- ✓ A proportion means that two ratios are equal. It can be written in two ways:
  $$\frac{a}{b} = \frac{c}{d}, a : b = c : d$$
- ✓ The proportion $\frac{a}{b} = \frac{c}{d}$ can be written as: $a \times d = c \times b$

Examples:

1) Solve this proportion for x. $\frac{4}{8} = \frac{5}{x}$

Use cross multiplication: $\frac{4}{8} = \frac{5}{x} \Rightarrow 4 \times x = 5 \times 8 \Rightarrow 4x = 40$

Divide to find x: $x = \frac{40}{4} \Rightarrow x = 10$

2) If a box contains red and blue balls in ratio of $2 : 3$ red to blue, how many red balls are there if 90 blue balls are in the box?

Write a proportion and solve. $\frac{2}{3} = \frac{x}{90}$

Use cross multiplication: $2 \times 90 = 3 \times x \Rightarrow 180 = 3x$

Divide to find x: $x = \frac{180}{3} \Rightarrow x = 60$

Create a Proportion

Step-by-step guide:

- ✓ A proportion contains two equal fractions! A proportion simply means that two fractions are equal.
- ✓ To create a proportion, simply find (or create) two equal fractions.

Examples:

1) Express ratios as a Proportion.
120 miles on 4 gallons of gas, how many miles on 1 gallon of gas?

First create a fraction: $\frac{120 \ miles}{4 \ gallons}$, and divide: $120 \div 4 = 30$

Then: 30 miles per gallon

2) State if this pair of ratios form a proportion. $\frac{3}{5} \ and \ \frac{24}{45}$

Use cross multiplication: $\frac{3}{5} = \frac{24}{45} \to 3 \times 45 = 5 \times 24 \to 135 = 120$, which is not correct.
Therefore, this pair of ratios doesn't form a proportion.

Similarity and Ratios

Step-by-step guide:

✓ Two or more figures are similar if the corresponding angles are equal, and the corresponding sides are in proportion.

Examples:

1) A girl 160 *cm* tall, stands 360 *cm* from a lamp post at night. Her shadow from the light is 90 *cm* long. How high is the lamp post?

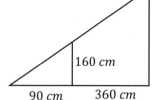

Write the proportion and solve for missing side.

$$\frac{\text{Smaller triangle height}}{\text{Smaller triangle base}} = \frac{\text{Bigger triangle height}}{\text{Bigger triangle base}}$$

$$\Rightarrow \frac{90cm}{160cm} = \frac{90+360cm}{x} \Rightarrow 90x = 160 \times 450 \Rightarrow x = 800 \ cm$$

2) A tree 32 *feet* tall casts a shadow 12 *feet* long. Jack is 6 *feet* tall. How long is Jack's shadow?

Write a proportion and solve for the missing number.

$$\frac{32}{12} = \frac{6}{x} \rightarrow 32x = 6 \times 12 = 72$$

$$32x = 72 \rightarrow x = \frac{72}{32} = 2.25 \ feet$$

Day 2 Practices

Find each sum or difference.

1) $15 + (-8) =$

2) $(-11) + (-21) =$

3) $7 + (-27) =$

4) $45 + (-14) =$

5) $(-8) + (-12) + 6 =$

6) $37 + (-16) + 12 =$

Find each product or quotient.

7) $(-7) \times (-8) =$

8) $4 \times (-5) =$

9) $5 \times (-11) =$

10) $(-5) \times (-20) =$

11) $-(2) \times (-8) \times 3 =$

12) $(12 - 4) \times (-10) =$

Order each set of integers from least to greatest.

13) $7, -9, -6, -1, 3$ ___, ___, ___, ___, ___, ___

14) $-4, -11, 5, 12, 9$ ___, ___, ___, ___, ___, ___

15) $18, -12, -19, 21, -20$ ___, ___, ___, ___, ___, ___

16) $-15, -25, 18, -7, 32$ ___, ___, ___, ___, ___, ___

Evaluate each expression.

17) $5 + (6 \times 3) =$

18) $13 - (2 \times 5) =$

19) $(14 \times 2) + 18 =$

20) $(12 - 5) - (4 \times 3) =$

21) $25 + (14 \div 2) =$

22) $(18 \times 5) \div 2 =$

✎ Evaluate the value.

23) $8 - |4 - 18| - |-2| =$

24) $|-2| - \frac{|-20|}{4} =$

25) $\frac{|-66|}{11} \times |-6| =$

26) $\frac{|-5 \times -3|}{5} \times \frac{|-20|}{4} =$

27) $|2 \times -4| + \frac{|-40|}{5} =$

28) $\frac{|-28|}{4} \times \frac{|-55|}{11} =$

✎ Reduce each ratio.

29) $24 : 16 =$ ___ : ___

30) $4 : 40 =$ ___ : ___

31) $6 : 72 =$ ___ : ___

32) $18 : 36 =$ ___ : ___

33) $6 : 100 =$ ___ : ___

34) $4 : 24 =$ ___ : ___

✎ Solve each proportion.

35) $\frac{4}{10} = \frac{14}{x}, x =$ ____

36) $\frac{2}{12} = \frac{7}{x}, x =$ ____

37) $\frac{3}{5} = \frac{27}{x}, x =$ ____

38) $\frac{1}{5} = \frac{x}{80}, x =$ ____

39) $\frac{3}{7} = \frac{x}{63}, x =$ ____

40) $\frac{2}{8} = \frac{13}{x}, x =$ ____

✎ State if each pair of ratios form a proportion.

41) $\frac{6}{20}$ and $\frac{9}{30}$

42) $\frac{1}{2}$ and $\frac{16}{32}$

43) $\frac{10}{12}$ and $\frac{35}{42}$

44) $\frac{3}{7}$ and $\frac{27}{72}$

45) $\frac{2}{5}$ and $\frac{16}{45}$

46) $\frac{8}{18}$ and $\frac{40}{81}$

✎ Solve each problem.

47) Two rectangles are similar. The first is 6 *feet* wide and 20 *feet* long. The second is 15 *feet* wide. What is the length of the second rectangle? _____

48) Two rectangles are similar. One is 2.5 *meters* by 9 *meters*. The longer side of the second rectangle is 22.5 *meters*. What is the other side of the second rectangle? _____

Answers

1) 7
2) −32
3) −20
4) 31
5) −14
6) 33
7) 56
8) −20
9) −55
10) 100
11) 48
12) −80
13) −9, −6, −1, 3, 7
14) −11, −4, 5, 9, 12
15) −20, −19, −12, 18, 21
16) −25, −15, −7, 18, 32

17) 23
18) 3
19) 46
20) −5
21) 32
22) 45
23) −8
24) −3
25) 36
26) 15
27) 16
28) 35
29) 3 : 2
30) 1 : 10
31) 1 : 12
32) 1 : 2

33) 3 : 50
34) 1 : 6
35) 35
36) 42
37) 45
38) 16
39) 27
40) 52
41) Yes
42) Yes
43) Yes
44) No
45) No
46) No
47) 50 feet
48) 6.25 meters

Day 3:
Percentage, Exponents, Variables and Roots

Math Topics that you'll learn today:

- ✓ Percentage Calculations
- ✓ Percent Problems
- ✓ Percent of Increase and Decrease
- ✓ Discount, Tax and Tip
- ✓ Simple Interest
- ✓ Multiplication Property of Exponents
- ✓ Division Property of Exponents
- ✓ Powers of Products and Quotients
- ✓ Zero and Negative Exponents
- ✓ Negative Exponents and Negative Bases
- ✓ Scientific Notation
- ✓ Square Roots

Mathematics is no more computation than typing is literature. - John Allen Paulos

Percentage Calculations

Step-by-step guide:

- ✓ Percent is a ratio of a number and 100. It always has the same denominator, 100. Percent symbol is %.
- ✓ Percent is another way to write decimals or fractions. For example:
$$40\% = 0.40 = \frac{40}{100} = \frac{2}{5}$$
- ✓ Use the following formula to find part, whole, or percent:
$$\text{part} = \frac{\text{percent}}{100} \times \text{whole}$$

Examples:

1) What is 10% of 45? Use the following formula: $\text{part} = \frac{\text{percent}}{100} \times \text{whole}$

$\text{part} = \frac{10}{100} \times 45 \rightarrow \text{part} = \frac{1}{10} \times 45 \rightarrow \text{part} = \frac{45}{10} \rightarrow \text{part} = 4.5$

2) What is 15% of 24? Use the percent formula: $\text{part} = \frac{\text{percent}}{100} \times \text{whole}$

$\text{part} = \frac{15}{100} \times 24 \rightarrow \text{part} = \frac{360}{100} \rightarrow \text{part} = 3.6$

Percent Problems

Step-by-step guide:

- ✓ In each percent problem, we are looking for the base, or part or the percent.
- ✓ Use the following equations to find each missing section.
  - o Base = Part ÷ Percent
  - o Part = Percent × Base
  - o Percent = Part ÷ Base

Examples:

1) 1.2 is what percent of 24?
   In this problem, we are looking for the percent. Use the following equation:
$$Percent = Part \div Base \rightarrow Percent = 1.2 \div 24 = 0.05 = 5\%$$

2) 20 is 5% of what number?

Use the following formula: $Base = Part \div Percent \rightarrow Base = 20 \div 0.05 = 400$
20 is 5% of 400.

Percent of Increase and Decrease

Step-by-step guide:

   To find the percentage of increase or decrease:
   ✓ New Number – Original Number
   ✓ The result ÷ Original Number × 100
   ✓ If your answer is a negative number, then this is a percentage decrease. If it is positive, then this is a percent of increase.

Examples:

1) Increased by 50%, the numbers 84 becomes:

   First find 50% of 84 → $\frac{50}{100} \times 84 = \frac{50 \times 84}{100} = 42$

   Then: $84 + 42 = 126$

2) The price of a shirt increases from \$10 to \$14. What is the percent increase?
   First: $14 - 10 = 4$
   4 is the result. Then: $4 \div 10 = \frac{4}{10} = 0.4 = 40\%$

Discount, Tax and Tip

Step-by-step guide:

   ✓ Discount = Multiply the regular price by the rate of discount
   ✓ Selling price = original price – discount
   ✓ Tax: To find tax, multiply the tax rate to the taxable amount (income, property value, etc.)
   ✓ To find tip, multiply the rate to the selling price.

Examples:

1) With an 10% discount, Ella was able to save \$20 on a dress. What was the original price of the dress?
   $10\% \ of \ x = \ 20, \frac{10}{100} \times x = \ 20, x = \frac{100 \times 20}{10} = 200$

2) Sophia purchased a sofa for $530.40. The sofa is regularly priced at $624. What was the percent discount Sophia received on the sofa?

Use this formula: $percent = Part \div base = 530.40 \div 624 = 0.85 = 85\%$

Therefore, the discount is: $100\% - 85\% = 15\%$

Simple Interest

Step-by-step guide:

✓ Simple Interest: The charge for borrowing money or the return for lending it. To solve a simple interest problem, use this formula:

Interest = principal × rate × time $\Rightarrow$ $I = p \times r \times t$

Examples:

1) Find simple interest for $450 investment at 7% for 8 years.

Use Interest formula: $I = prt$, $P = \$450$, $r = 7\% = \frac{7}{100} = 0.07$ and $t = 8$

Then: $I = 450 \times 0.07 \times 8 = \$252$

2) Find simple interest for $5,200 at 4% for 3 years.

Use Interest formula: $I = prt$, $P = \$5,200$, $r = 4\% = \frac{4}{100} = 0.04$ and $t = 3$

Then: $I = 5,200 \times 0.04 \times 3 = \$624$

Multiplication Property of Exponents

Step-by-step guide:

✓ Exponents are shorthand for repeated multiplication of the same number by itself. For example, instead of 2×2, we can write 2^2. For $3 \times 3 \times 3 \times 3$, we can write 3^4

✓ In algebra, a variable is a letter used to stand for a number. The most common letters are: $x, y, z, a, b, c, m,$ and n.

✓ Exponent's rules: $x^a \times x^b = x^{a+b}$, $\frac{x^a}{x^b} = x^{a-b}$

$$(x^a)^b = x^{a \times b}, \qquad (xy)^a = x^a \times y^a, \left(\frac{a}{b}\right)^c = \frac{a^c}{b^c}$$

Examples:

1) Multiply. $-2x^5 \times 7x^3 =$
   Use Exponent's rules: $x^a \times x^b = x^{a+b} \rightarrow x^5 \times x^3 = x^{5+3} = x^8$
   Then: $-2x^5 \times 7x^3 = -14x^8$

2) Multiply. $(x^2y^4)^3 =$
   Use Exponent's rules: $(x^a)^b = x^{a \times b}$. Then: $(x^2y^4)^3 = x^{2 \times 3}y^{4 \times 3} = x^6y^{12}$

Division Property of Exponents

Step-by-step guide:

✓ For division of exponents use these formulas: $\dfrac{x^a}{x^b} = x^{a-b}$, $x \neq 0$

$$\frac{x^a}{x^b} = \frac{1}{x^{b-a}}, x \neq 0, \qquad \frac{1}{x^b} = x^{-b}$$

Examples:

1) Simplify. $\dfrac{4x^3y}{36x^2y^3} =$

   First cancel the common factor: $4 \rightarrow \dfrac{4x^3y}{36x^2y^3} = \dfrac{x^3y}{9x^2y^3}$

   Use Exponent's rules: $\dfrac{x^a}{x^b} = x^{a-b} \rightarrow \dfrac{x^3}{x^2} = x^{3-2}$

   Then: $\dfrac{4x^3y}{36x^2y^3} = \dfrac{xy}{9y^3} \rightarrow$ now cancel the common factor: $y \rightarrow \dfrac{xy}{9y^3} = \dfrac{x}{9y^2}$

2) Divide. $\dfrac{2x^{-5}}{9x^{-2}} =$

   Use Exponent's rules: $\dfrac{x^a}{x^b} = \dfrac{1}{x^{b-a}} \rightarrow \dfrac{x^{-5}}{x^{-2}} = \dfrac{1}{x^{-2-(-5)}} = \dfrac{1}{x^{-2+5}} = \dfrac{1}{x^3}$

   Then: $\dfrac{2x^{-5}}{9x^{-2}} = \dfrac{2}{9x^3}$

Powers of Products and Quotients

Step-by-step guide:

✓ For any nonzero numbers a and b and any integer x, $(ab)^x = a^x \times b^x$.

Examples:

1) Simplify. $(3x^5y^4)^2 =$

Use Exponent's rules: $(x^a)^b = x^{a \times b}$

$(3x^5y^4)^2 = (3)^2(x^5)^2(y^4)^2 = 9x^{5 \times 2}y^{4 \times 2} = 9x^{10}y^8$

2) Simplify. $(\frac{2x}{3x^2})^2 =$ First cancel the common factor: $x \to (\frac{2x}{3x^2})^2 = (\frac{2}{3x})^2$

Use Exponent's rules: $(\frac{a}{b})^c = \frac{a^c}{b^c}$, Then: $(\frac{2}{3x})^2 = \frac{2^2}{(3x)^2} = \frac{4}{9x^2}$

Zero and Negative Exponents

Step-by-step guide:

✓ A negative exponent simply means that the base is on the wrong side of the fraction line, so you need to flip the base to the other side. For instance, "x^{-2}" (pronounced as "ecks to the minus two") just means "x^2" but underneath, as in $\frac{1}{x^2}$.

Examples:

1) Evaluate. $(\frac{4}{9})^{-2} =$

Use Exponent's rules: $\frac{1}{x^b} = x^{-b} \to (\frac{4}{9})^{-2} = \frac{1}{(\frac{4}{9})^2} = \frac{1}{\frac{4^2}{9^2}}$

Now use fraction rule: $\frac{1}{\frac{b}{c}} = \frac{c}{b} \to \frac{1}{\frac{4^2}{9^2}} = \frac{9^2}{4^2} = \frac{81}{16}$

2) Evaluate. $(\frac{5}{6})^{-3} =$

Use Exponent's rules: $\frac{1}{x^b} = x^{-b} \to (\frac{5}{6})^{-3} = \frac{1}{(\frac{5}{6})^3} = \frac{1}{\frac{5^3}{6^3}}$, Now use fraction rule: $\frac{1}{\frac{b}{c}} = \frac{c}{b} \to \frac{1}{\frac{5^3}{6^3}} =$

$\frac{6^3}{5^3} = \frac{216}{125}$

Negative Exponents and Negative Bases

Step-by-step guide:

- ✓ Make the power positive. A negative exponent is the reciprocal of that number with a positive exponent.
- ✓ The parenthesis is important!
- ✓ 5^{-2} is not the same as $(-5)^{-2}$

$$(-5)^{-2} = -\frac{1}{5^2} \text{ and } (-5)^{-2} = +\frac{1}{5^2}$$

Examples:

1) Simplify. $(\frac{3a}{2c})^{-2} =$

Use Exponent's rules: $\frac{1}{x^b} = x^{-b} \rightarrow (\frac{3a}{2c})^{-2} = \frac{1}{(\frac{3a}{2c})^2} = \frac{1}{\frac{3^2 a^2}{2^2 c^2}}$

Now use fraction rule: $\frac{\frac{1}{b}}{c} = \frac{c}{b} \rightarrow \frac{1}{\frac{3^2 a^2}{2^2 c^2}} = \frac{2^2 c^2}{3^2 a^2}$

Then: $\frac{2^2 c^2}{3^2 a^2} = \frac{4c^2}{9a^2}$

2) Simplify. $(-\frac{5x}{3yz})^{-3} =$

Use Exponent's rules: $\frac{1}{x^b} = x^{-b} \rightarrow (-\frac{5x}{3yz})^{-3} = \frac{1}{(-\frac{5x}{3yz})^3} = \frac{1}{-\frac{5^3 x^3}{3^3 y^3 z^3}}$

Now use fraction rule: $\frac{\frac{1}{b}}{c} = \frac{c}{b} \rightarrow \frac{1}{-\frac{5^3 x^3}{3^3 y^3 z^3}} = -\frac{3^3 y^3 z^3}{5^3 x^3} = -\frac{27y^3 z^3}{125x^3}$

Scientific Notation

Step-by-step guide:

- ✓ It is used to write very big or very small numbers in decimal form.
- ✓ In scientific notation all numbers are written in the form of:

$$m \times 10^n$$

Decimal notation	Scientific notation
5	5×10^0
$-25,000$	-2.5×10^4
0.5	5×10^{-1}
2,122.456	$2,122456 \times 10^3$

Examples:

1) Write **0.00012** in scientific notation.

First, move the decimal point to the right so that you have a number that is between 1 and 10. Then: $N = 1.2$

Second, determine how many places the decimal moved in step 1 by the power of 10. Then: $10^{-4} \rightarrow$ When the decimal moved to the right, the exponent is negative.

Then: $0.00012 = 1.2 \times 10^{-4}$

2) Write **8.3 × 10^{−5}** in standard notation.

$10^{-5} \rightarrow$ When the decimal moved to the right, the exponent is negative.

Then: $8.3 \times 10^{-5} = 0.000083$

Square Roots

Step-by-step guide:

✓ A square root of x is a number r whose square is: $r^2 = x$

r is a square root of x.

Examples:

1) Find the square root of $\sqrt{225}$.

First factor the number: $225 = 15^2$, Then: $\sqrt{225} = \sqrt{15^2}$

Now use radical rule: $\sqrt[n]{a^n} = a$

Then: $\sqrt{15^2} = 15$

2) Evaluate. $\sqrt{4} \times \sqrt{16} =$

First factor the numbers: $4 = 2^2$ and $16 = 4^2$

Then: $\sqrt{4} \times \sqrt{16} = \sqrt{2^2} \times \sqrt{4^2}$

Now use radical rule: $\sqrt[n]{a^n} = a$, Then: $\sqrt{2^2} \times \sqrt{4^2} = 2 \times 4 = 8$

Day 3 Practices

✍ *Calculate the given percent of each value.*

1) 5% of 60 = ____
2) 10% of 30 = ____
3) 20% of 25 = ____

4) 50% of 80 = ____
5) 40% of 200 = ____
6) 20% of 45 = ____

✍ *Solve each problem.*

7) 20 is what percent of 50? ____%
8) 18 is what percent of 90? ____%
9) 12 is what percent of 15? ____%

10) 16 is what percent of 200? ____%
11) 24 is what percent of 800? ____%
12) 48 is what percent of 400? ____%

✍ *Solve each percent of change word problem.*

13) Bob got a raise, and his hourly wage increased from $12 to $15. What is the percent increase? _____ %

14) The price of a pair of shoes increases from $20 to $32. What is the percent increase? ____ %

✍ *Find the selling price of each item.*

15) Original price of a computer: $500
Tax: 6%, Selling price: $_____

16) Original price of a laptop: $350
Tax: 8%, Selling price: $_____

✍ *Determine the simple interest for these loans.*

17) $1,300 at 5% for 6 years. $ _____
18) $5,400 at 3.5% for 6 months. $ _____

✍ *Simplify and write the answer in exponential form.*

19) $2yx^3 \times 4x^2y^3 =$
20) $4x^2 \times 9x^3y^4 =$
21) $7x^4y^5 \times 3x^2y^3 =$

22) $9x^2y^5 \times 7xy^3 =$
23) $4xy^4 \times 7x^3y^3 =$
24) $8x^2y^3 \times 3x^5y^3 =$

✍ Simplify. (Division Property of Exponents)

25) $\frac{3^7 \times 3^4}{3^8 \times 3^2} =$

26) $\frac{5x}{10x^3} =$

27) $\frac{6x^3}{4x^5} =$

28) $\frac{24x^3}{28x^6} =$

29) $\frac{24x^3}{18y^8} =$

30) $\frac{50xy^4}{10y^2} =$

✍ Simplify. (Powers of Products and Quotients)

31) $(9x^7y^5)^2 =$

32) $(4x^4y^6)^5 =$

33) $(3x \times 4y^3)^2 =$

34) $(\frac{5x}{x^2})^2 =$

35) $\left(\frac{x^4y^4}{x^2y^2}\right)^3 =$

36) $\left(\frac{25x}{5x^6}\right)^2 =$

✍ Evaluate the following expressions. (Zero and Negative Exponents)

37) $2^{-3} =$

38) $3^{-3} =$

39) $7^{-3} =$

40) $6^{-3} =$

41) $8^{-3} =$

42) $9^{-2} =$

✍ Simplify. (Negative Exponents and Negative Bases)

43) $-5x^{-2}y^{-3} =$

44) $20x^{-4}y^{-1} =$

45) $14a^{-6}b^{-7} =$

46) $-12x^2y^{-3} =$

47) $-\frac{25}{x^{-6}} =$

48) $\frac{7b}{-9c^{-4}} =$

✍ Write each number in scientific notation.

49) $0.000325 =$

50) $0.00023 =$

51) $56,000,000 =$

52) $21,000 =$

✍ Evaluate.

53) $\sqrt{9} \times \sqrt{4} =$ _____

54) $\sqrt{64} \times \sqrt{25} =$ _____

55) $\sqrt{8} \times \sqrt{2} =$ _____

56) $\sqrt{6} \times \sqrt{6} =$ _____

57) $\sqrt{5} \times \sqrt{5} =$ _____

58) $\sqrt{8} \times \sqrt{8} =$ _____

Answers

1) 3
2) 3
3) 5
4) 40
5) 80
6) 9
7) 40%
8) 20%
9) 80%
10) 8%
11) 3%
12) 12%
13) 25%
14) 60%
15) $530.00
16) $378.00
17) $390.00
18) $94.50
19) $8x^5y^4$
20) $36x^5y^4$
21) $21x^6y^8$
22) $63x^3y^8$

23) $28x^4y^7$
24) $24x^7y^6$
25) 3
26) $\frac{1}{2x^2}$
27) $\frac{3}{2x^2}$
28) $\frac{6}{7x^3}$
29) $\frac{4x^3}{3y^8}$
30) $5xy^2$
31) $81x^{14}y^{10}$
32) $1,024x^{20}y^{30}$
33) $144x^2y^6$
34) $\frac{25}{x^2}$
35) x^6y^6
36) $\frac{25}{x^{10}}$
37) $\frac{1}{8}$
38) $\frac{1}{27}$
39) $\frac{1}{343}$
40) $\frac{1}{216}$

41) $\frac{1}{512}$
42) $\frac{1}{81}$
43) $-\frac{5}{x^2y^3}$
44) $\frac{20}{x^4y}$
45) $\frac{14}{a^6b^7}$
46) $-\frac{12x^2}{y^3}$
47) $-25x^6$
48) $-\frac{7bc^4}{9}$
49) 3.25×10^{-4}
50) 2.3×10^{-4}
51) 5.6×10^7
52) 2.1×10^4
53) 6
54) 40
55) 4
56) 6
57) 5
58) 8

Day 4:
Expressions, Variables, Equations and Inequalities

Math Topics that you'll learn today:

- ✓ Simplifying Variable Expressions
- ✓ Simplifying Polynomial Expressions
- ✓ The Distributive Property
- ✓ Evaluating One Variable
- ✓ Evaluating Two Variables

- ✓ Combining like Terms
- ✓ One–Step Equations
- ✓ Multi–Step Equations
- ✓ Graphing Single–Variable Inequalities
- ✓ One–Step Inequalities
- ✓ Multi–Step Inequalities

Mathematics is, as it were, a sensuous logic, and relates to philosophy as do the arts, music, and plastic art to poetry. ~ K.

Shegel

Simplifying Variable Expressions

Step-by-step guide:

- ✓ In algebra, a variable is a letter used to stand for a number. The most common letters are: $x, y, z, a, b, c, m, and\ n$.
- ✓ algebraic expression is an expression contains integers, variables, and the math operations such as addition, subtraction, multiplication, division, etc.
- ✓ In an expression, we can combine "like" terms. (values with same variable and same power)

Examples:

1) Simplify this expression. $(10x + 2x + 3) =$?
   Combine like terms. Then: $(10x + 2x + 3) = 12x + 3$ (remember you cannot combine variables and numbers.
2) Simplify this expression. $12 - 3x^2 + 9x + 5x^2 =$?
   Combine "like" terms: $-3x^2 + 5x^2 = 2x^2$

   Then: $12 - 3x^2 + 9x + 5x^2 = 12 + 2x^2 + 9x$. Write in standard form (biggest powers first): $2x^2 + 9x + 12$

Simplifying Polynomial Expressions

Step-by-step guide:

- ✓ In mathematics, a polynomial is an expression consisting of variables and coefficients that involves only the operations of addition, subtraction, multiplication, and non-negative integer exponents of variables.
   $$P(x) = a_n x^n + a_{n-1} x^{n-1} + \dots + a_2 x^2 + a_1 x + a_0$$

Examples:

1) Simplify this Polynomial Expressions. $4x^2 - 5x^3 + 15x^4 - 12x^3 =$
   Combine "like" terms: $-5x^3 - 12x^3 = -17x^3$
   Then: $4x^2 - 5x^3 + 15x^4 - 12x^3 = 4x^2 - 17x^3 + 15x^4$
   Then write in standard form: $4x^2 - 17x^3 + 15x^4 = 15x^4 - 17x^3 + 4x^2$

2) Simplify this expression. $(2x^2 - x^4) - (4x^4 - x^2) =$
   First use distributive property: → multiply $(-)$ into $(4x^4 - x^2)$
   $(2x^2 - x^4) - (4x^4 - x^2) = 2x^2 - x^4 - 4x^4 + x^2$

Then combine "like" terms: $2x^2 - x^4 - 4x^4 + x^2 = 3x^2 - 5x^4$

And write in standard form: $3x^2 - 5x^4 = -5x^4 + 3x^2$

The Distributive Property

Step-by-step guide:

✓ Distributive Property: $a(b + c) = ab + ac$

Examples:

1) Simply. $(5x - 3)(-5) =$

   Use Distributive Property formula: $a(b + c) = ab + ac$
   $(5x - 3)(-5) = -25x + 15$

2) Simply $(-8)(2x - 8) =$

   Use Distributive Property formula: $a(b + c) = ab + ac$
   $(-8)(2x - 8) = -16x + 64$

Evaluating One Variable

Step-by-step guide:

✓ To evaluate one variable expression, find the variable and substitute a number for that variable.
✓ Perform the arithmetic operations.

Examples:

1) Solve this expression. $12 - 2x$, $x = -1$

   First substitute -1 for x, then:

   $12 - 2x = 12 - 2(-1) = 12 + 2 = 14$

2) Solve this expression. $-8 + 5x$, $x = 3$

   First substitute 3 for x, then: $-8 + 5x = -8 + 5(3) = -8 + 15 = 7$

Evaluating Two Variables

Step-by-step guide:

✓ To evaluate an algebraic expression, substitute a number for each variable and perform the arithmetic operations.

Examples:

1) Solve this expression. $-3x + 5y$, $x = 2, y = -1$

First substitute 2 for x, and -1 for y , then:

$-3x + 5y = -3(2) + 5(-1) = -6 - 5 = -11$

2) Solve this expression. $2(a - 2b), a = -1, b = 3$

First substitute -1 for a, and 3 for b , then:

$2(a - 2b) = 2a - 4b = 2(-1) - 4(3) = -2 - 12 = -14$

Combining like Terms

Step-by-step guide:

✓ Terms are separated by "+" and "−" signs.
✓ Like terms are terms with same variables and same powers.
✓ Be sure to use the "+" or "−" that is in front of the coefficient.

Examples:

1) Simplify this expression. $(-5)(8x - 6) =$

Use Distributive Property formula: $a(b + c) = ab + ac$
$(-5)(8x - 6) = -40x + 30$

2) Simplify this expression. $(-3)(2x - 2) + 6 =$

First use Distributive Property formula: $a(b + c) = ab + ac$
$(-3)(2x - 2) + 6 = -6x + 6 + 6$

And Combining like Terms:

$-6x + 6 + 6 = -6x + 12$

One–Step Equations

Step-by-step guide:

✓ The values of two expressions on both sides of an equation are equal. $ax + b = c$
✓ You only need to perform one Math operation in order to solve the one-step equations.
✓ To solve one-step equation, find the inverse (opposite) operation is being performed.
✓ The inverse operations are:
  - Addition and subtraction
  - Multiplication and division

Examples:

1) Solve this equation. $x + 24 = 0 , x = ?$
   Here, the operation is addition and its inverse operation is subtraction. To solve this equation, subtract 24 from both sides of the equation: $x + 24 - 24 = 0 - 24$
   Then simplify: $x + 24 - 24 = 0 - 24 \rightarrow x = -24$

2) Solve this equation. $3x = 15, x = ?$
   Here, the operation is multiplication (variable x is multiplied by 3) and its inverse operation is division. To solve this equation, divide both sides of equation by 3:
   $$3x = 15 \rightarrow 3x \div 3 = 15 \div 3 \rightarrow x = 5$$

Multi–Step Equations

Step-by-step guide:

✓ Combine "like" terms on one side.
✓ Bring variables to one side by adding or subtracting.
✓ Simplify using the inverse of addition or subtraction.
✓ Simplify further by using the inverse of multiplication or division.

Examples:

1) Solve this equation. $-(2 - x) = 5$

   First use Distributive Property: $-(2 - x) = -2 + x$
   Now solve by adding 2 to both sides of the equation. $-2 + x = 5 \rightarrow -2 + x + 2 = 5 + 2$

Now simplify: $-2 + x + 2 = 5 + 2 \rightarrow x = 7$

2) Solve this equation. $4x + 10 = 25 - x$

First bring variables to one side by adding x to both sides.
$4x + 10 + x = 25 - x + x \rightarrow 5x + 10 = 25$. Now, subtract 10 from both sides:
$5x + 10 - 10 = 25 - 10 \rightarrow 5x = 15$
Now, divide both sides by 5: $5x = 15 \rightarrow 5x \div 5 = \frac{15}{5} \rightarrow x = 3$

Graphing Single–Variable Inequalities

Step-by-step guide:

- ✓ Inequality is similar to equations and uses symbols for "less than" (<) and "greater than" (>).
- ✓ To solve inequalities, we need to isolate the variable. (like in equations)
- ✓ To graph an inequality, find the value of the inequality on the number line.
- ✓ For less than or greater than draw open circle on the value of the variable.
- ✓ If there is an equal sign too, then use filled circle.
- ✓ Draw a line to the right or to the left for greater or less than.

Examples:

1) Draw a graph for $x > 2$

Since, the variable is greater than
2, then we need to find 2 and draw
an open circle above it. Then, draw a line to the right.

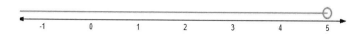

2) Graph this inequality. $x < 5$

One–Step Inequalities

Step-by-step guide:

- ✓ Similar to equations, first isolate the variable by using inverse operation.
- ✓ For dividing or multiplying both sides by negative numbers, flip the direction of the inequality sign.

Examples:

Multi–Step Inequalities

1) Solve and graph the inequality. $x + 2 \geq 3$.

Subtract 2 from both sides. $x + 2 \geq 3 \rightarrow x + 2 - 2 \geq 3 - 2$, then: $x \geq 1$

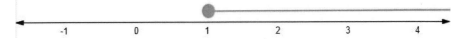

2) Solve this inequality. $x - 1 \leq 2$

Add 1 to both sides. $x - 1 \leq 2 \rightarrow x - 1 + 1 \leq 2 + 1$, then: $x \leq 3$

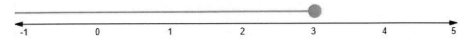

Step-by-step guide:

- ✓ Isolate the variable.
- ✓ Simplify using the inverse of addition or subtraction.
- ✓ Simplify further by using the inverse of multiplication or division.

Examples:

1) Solve this inequality. $2x - 2 \leq 6$

First add 2 to both sides: $2x - 2 + 2 \leq 6 + 2 \rightarrow 2x \leq 8$

Now, divide both sides by 2: $2x \leq 8 \rightarrow x \leq 4$

2) Solve this inequality. $2x - 4 \leq 8$

First add 4 to both sides: $2x - 4 + 4 \leq 8 + 4$

Then simplify: $2x - 4 + 4 \leq 8 + 4 \rightarrow 2x \leq 12$

Now divide both sides by 2: $\frac{2x}{2} \leq \frac{12}{2} \rightarrow x \leq 6$

Day 4 Practices

✎ Simplify each expression.

1) $(2x + x + 8 + 19) =$

2) $(-22x - 26x + 24) =$

3) $8x + 3 - 4x =$

4) $-2 - 5x^2 - 2x^2 =$

5) $3 + 10x^2 + 2 =$

6) $3x^2 + 6x + 12x^2 =$

✎ Simplify each polynomial.

7) $(2x^3 + 5x^2) - (12x + 2x^2) =$ _____

8) $(2x^5 + 2x^3) - (7x^3 + 6x^2) =$ _____

9) $(12x^4 + 4x^2) - (2x^2 - 6x^4) =$ _____

✎ Use the distributive property to simply each expression.

10) $2(2 + 3x) =$

11) $3(5 + 5x) =$

12) $4(3x - 8) =$

13) $(6x - 2)(-2) =$

14) $(-3)(x + 2) =$

15) $(2 + 2x)5 =$

✎ Evaluate each expression using the value given.

16) $5 + x , x = 2$

17) $x - 2, x = 4$

18) $8x + 1, x = 9$

19) $x - 12, x = -1$

20) $9 - x , x = 3$

21) $x + 2, x = 5$

✎ Evaluate each expression using the values given.

22) $2x + 4y, x = 3, y = 2$

23) $8x + 5y, x = 1, y = 5$

24) $-2a + 4b, a = 6, b = 3$

25) $4x + 7 - 2y, x = 7, y = 6$

✍ **Simplify each expression. (Combining like Terms)**

26) $2x + x + 2 =$

27) $2(5x - 3) =$

28) $7x - 2x + 8 =$

29) $(-4)(3x - 5) =$

30) $9x - 7x - 5 =$

31) $16x - 5 + 8x =$

✍ **Solve each equation. (One–Step Equations)**

32) $16 = -4 + x, x =$ ____

33) $x - 4 = -25, x =$ ____

34) $x + 12 = -9, x =$ ____

35) $14 = 18 - x, x =$ ____

36) $2 + x = -14, x =$ ____

37) $x - 5 = 15, x =$ ____

✍ **Solve each equation. (Multi–Step Equations)**

38) $-3(2 + x) = 3$

39) $-2(4 + x) = 4$

40) $20 = -(x - 8)$

41) $2(2 - 2x) = 20$

42) $-12 = -(2x + 8)$

43) $5(2 + x) = 5$

✍ **Draw a graph for each inequality.**

44) $x > -1$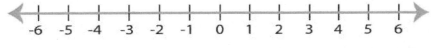

45) $x < 3$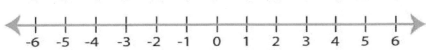

✍ **Solve each inequality and graph it.**

46) $2x \geq 12$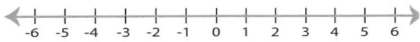

47) $4 + x \leq 5$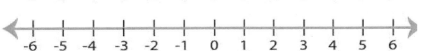

✍ **Solve each inequality.**

48) $4x - 16 \leq 12$

49) $16x - 4 \leq 28$

50) $-15 + 9x \leq 30$

51) $2(x - 3) \leq 6$

52) $14x - 10 \leq 18$

53) $8x - 42 < 38$

Answers

1) $3x + 27$
2) $-48x + 24$
3) $4x + 3$
10) $6x + 4$
11) $15x + 15$
16) 7
17) 2
22) 14
23) 33
26) $3x + 2$
27) $10x - 6$
32) 20
33) -21
38) -3
39) -6

4) $-7x^2 - 2$
5) $10x^2 + 5$
6) $15x^2 + 6x$
12) $12x - 32$
13) $-12x + 4$
18) 73
19) -13
24) 0
25) 23
28) $5x + 8$
29) $-12x + 20$
34) -21
35) 4
40) -12
41) -4

7) $2x^3 + 3x^2 - 12x$
8) $2x^5 - 5x^3 - 6x^2$
9) $18x^4 + 2x^2$
14) $-3x - 6$
15) $10x + 10$
20) 6
21) 7

30) $2x - 5$
31) $24x - 5$
36) -16
37) 20
42) 2
43) -1

44)

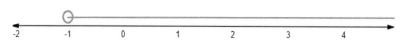

45)

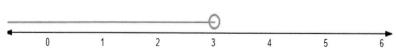

46)

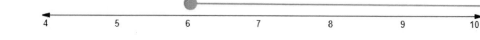

47)

48) $x \leq 7$
49) $x \leq 2$
50) $x \leq 5$

51) $x \leq 6$
52) $x \leq 2$
53) $x < 10$

Day 5:
Linear Equations and Inequalities

Math Topics that you'll learn today:

- ✓ Finding Slope

- ✓ Graphing Lines Using Slope–Intercept Form

- ✓ Graphing Lines Using Standard Form

- ✓ Writing Linear Equations

- ✓ Graphing Linear Inequalities

- ✓ Finding Midpoint

- ✓ Finding Distance of Two Points

"Nature is written in mathematical language." - Galileo Galilei

Finding Slope

Step-by-step guide:

- ✓ The slope of a line represents the direction of a line on the coordinate plane.
- ✓ A coordinate plane contains two perpendicular number lines. The horizontal line is x and the vertical line is y. The point at which the two axes intersect is called the origin. An ordered pair (x, y) shows the location of a point.
- ✓ A line on coordinate plane can be drawn by connecting two points.
- ✓ To find the slope of a line, we need two points.
- ✓ The slope of a line with two points A (x_1, y_1) and B (x_2, y_2) can be found by using this formula: $\frac{y_2 - y_1}{x_2 - x_1} = \frac{rise}{run}$

Examples:

1) Find the slope of the line through these two points: $(2, -10)$ *and* $(3, 6)$.

Slope $= \frac{y_2 - y_1}{x_2 - x_1}$. Let (x_1, y_1) be $(2, -10)$ and (x_2, y_2) be $(3, 6)$. Then: slope $= \frac{y_2 - y_1}{x_2 - x_1} = \frac{6-(-10)}{3-2} = \frac{6+10}{1} = \frac{16}{1} = 16$

2) Find the slope of the line containing two points $(8, 3)$ and $(-4, 9)$.

Slope $= \frac{y_2 - y_1}{x_2 - x_1} \rightarrow (x_1, y_1) = (8,3)$ and $(x_2, y_2) = (-4, 9)$. Then: slope $= \frac{y_2 - y_1}{x_2 - x_1} = \frac{9-3}{-4-8} = \frac{6}{-12} = \frac{1}{-2} = -\frac{1}{2}$

Graphing Lines Using Slope–Intercept Form

Step-by-step guide:

- ✓ Slope-intercept form of a line: given the slope m and the y-intercept (the intersection of the line and y-axis) b, then the equation of the line is:
$$y = mx + b$$

Example: *Sketch the graph of* $y = 8x - 3$.

To graph this line, we need to find two points. When x is zero the value of y is -3. And when y is zero the value of x is 3/8. $x = 0 \rightarrow y = 8(0) - 3 = -3$, $y = 0 \rightarrow 0 = 8x - 3 \rightarrow x = \frac{3}{8}$

Now, we have two points: $(0, -3)$ and $(\frac{3}{8}, 0)$. Find the points and graph the line. Remember that the slope of the line is 8.

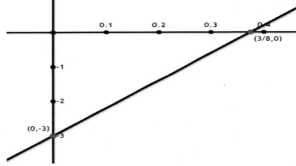

Graphing Lines Using Standard Form

Step-by-step guide:

- ✓ Find the x-intercept of the line by putting zero for y.
- ✓ Find the y-intercept of the line by putting zero for the x.
- ✓ Connect these two points.

Examples:

Sketch the graph of $x - y = -5$.

First isolate y for x: $x - y = -5 \rightarrow y = x + 5$
Find the x-intercept of the line by putting zero for y.
$y = x + 5 \rightarrow x + 5 = 0 \rightarrow x = -5$

Find the y-intercept of the line by putting zero for the x.
$y = 0 + 5 \rightarrow y = 5$

Then: x-intercept: $(-5, 0)$ and y-intercept: $(0, 5)$

Writing Linear Equations

Step-by-step guide:

- ✓ The equation of a line: $y = mx + b$
- ✓ Identify the slope.
- ✓ Find the y-intercept. This can be done by substituting the slope and the

coordinates of a point (x, y) on the line.

Examples:

1) What is the equation of the line that passes through $(2, -2)$ and has a slope of 7?

The general slope-intercept form of the equation of a line is $y = mx + b$, where m is the slope and b is the y-intercept.

By substitution of the given point and given slope, we have: $-2 = (2)(7) + b$

So, $b = -2 - 14 = -16$, and the required equation is $y = 7x - 16$.

2) Write the equation of the line through $(2, 1)$ and $(-1, 4)$.

$Slop = \frac{y_2 - y_1}{x_2 - x_1} = \frac{4 - 1}{-1 - 2} = \frac{3}{-3} = -1 \rightarrow m = -1$

To find the value of b, you can use either points. The answer will be the same: $y = -x + b$

$(2, 1) \rightarrow 1 = -2 + b \rightarrow b = 3$

$(-1, 4) \rightarrow 4 = -(-1) + b \rightarrow b = 3$

The equation of the line is: $y = -x + 3$

Graphing Linear Inequalities

Step-by-step guide:

- ✓ First, graph the "equals" line.
- ✓ Choose a testing point. (it can be any point on both sides of the line.)
- ✓ Put the value of (x, y) of that point in the inequality. If that works, that part of the line is the solution. If the values don't work, then the other part of the line is the solution.

Examples:

Sketch the graph of $y < 2x - 3$. First, graph the line:

$y = 2x - 3$. The slope is 2 and y-intercept is -3. Then, choose a testing point. The easiest point to test is the origin: $(0, 0)$

$$(0,0) \rightarrow y < 2x - 3 \rightarrow 0 < 2(0) - 3 \rightarrow 0 < -3$$

0 is not less than -3. So, the other part of the line (on the right side) is the solution.

Finding Midpoint

Step-by-step guide:

    ✓ The middle of a line segment is its midpoint.

    ✓ The Midpoint of two endpoints A (x_1, y_1) and B (x_2, y_2) can be found using this formula: M $(\frac{x_1+x_2}{2}, \frac{y_1+y_2}{2})$

Example:

1) Find the midpoint of the line segment with the given endpoints. $(4, -5), (0, 9)$

    Midpoint $= (\frac{x_1+x_2}{2}, \frac{y_1+y_2}{2}) \rightarrow (x_1, y_1) = (4, -5)$ and $(x_2, y_2) = (0, 9)$

    Midpoint $= (\frac{4+0}{2}, \frac{-5+9}{2}) \rightarrow (\frac{4}{2}, \frac{4}{2}) \rightarrow M(2, 2)$

2) Find the midpoint of the line segment with the given endpoints. $(6, 7), (4, -5)$

    Midpoint $= (\frac{x_1+x_2}{2}, \frac{y_1+y_2}{2}) \rightarrow (x_1, y_1) = (6, 7)$ and $(x_2, y_2) = (4, -5)$

    Midpoint $= (\frac{6+4}{2}, \frac{7-5}{2}) \rightarrow (\frac{10}{2}, \frac{2}{2}) \rightarrow (5, 1)$

Finding Distance of Two Points

Step-by-step guide:

    ✓ Distance of two points A (x_1, y_1) and B (x_2, y_2): $d = \sqrt{(x_1 - x_2)^2 + (y_1 - y_2)^2}$

Examples:

1) Find the distance between of $(0, 8), (-4, 5)$.

    Use distance of two points formula: $d = \sqrt{(x_1 - x_2)^2 + (y_1 - y_2)^2}$

    $(x_1, y_1) = (0, 8)$ and $(x_2, y_2) = (-4, 5)$. Then: $d = \sqrt{(x_1 - x_2)^2 + (y_1 - y_2)^2} \rightarrow$

    $d = \sqrt{(0 - (-4))^2 + (8 - 5)^2} = \sqrt{(4)^2 + (3)^2} = \sqrt{16 + 9} = \sqrt{25} = 5 \rightarrow d = 5$

2) Find the distance of two points $(4, 2)$ and $(-5, -10)$.

    Use distance of two points formula: $d = \sqrt{(x_1 - x_2)^2 + (y_1 - y_2)^2}$

    $(x_1, y_1) = (4, 2)$, and $(x_2, y_2) = (-5, -10)$

    Then: $d = \sqrt{(x_1 - x_2)^2 + (y_1 - y_2)^2} \rightarrow d = \sqrt{(4 - (-5))^2 + (2 - (-10))^2} =$

    $\sqrt{(9)^2 + (12)^2} = \sqrt{81 + 144} = \sqrt{225} = 15$. Then: $d = 15$

Day 5 Practices

✏️ *Find the slope of the line through each pair of points.*

1) $(1, 4), (3, 8)$

2) $(-1, 5), (0, 6)$

3) $(5, -5), (4, -1)$

4) $(-2, -1), (0, 5)$

5) $(5, 1), (2, 4)$

6) $(-3, 5), (-2, 8)$

✏️ *Sketch the graph of each line. (Using Slope–Intercept Form)*

7) $y = \frac{1}{2}x - 4$

8) $y = 2x$

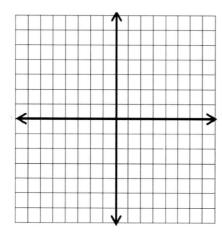

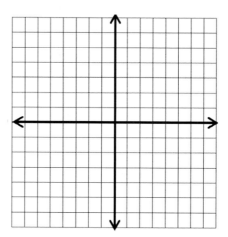

✏️ *Sketch the graph of each line. (Graphing Lines Using Standard Form)*

9) $y = 3x - 2$

10) $y = -x + 1$

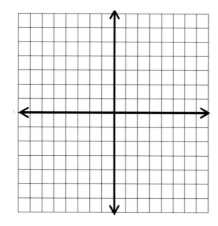

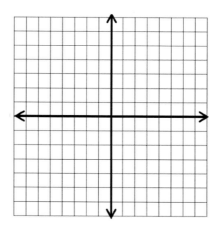

✍ *Write the equation of the line through the given points.*

11) through: $(1, -2), (-2, -17)$

12) through: $(-2, 1), (3, 6)$

13) through: $(-2, 1), (0, 5)$

14) through: $(5, 4), (2, 1)$

15) through: $(-4, 9), (3, 2)$

16) through: $(1, 0), (5, 20)$

✍ *Sketch the graph of each linear inequality. (Graphing Linear Inequalities)*

17) $2y > 6x - 2$

18) $3y < -3x + 12$

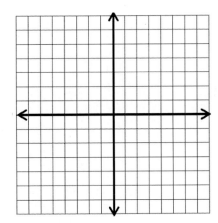
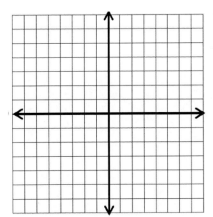

✍ *Find the midpoint of the line segment with the given endpoints.*

19) $(-4, -6), (2, 6)$

20) $(7, 4), (-4, 1)$

21) $(-4, -1), (8, 3)$

22) $(-5, 2), (1, 6)$

23) $(3, -2), (7, -6)$

24) $(-7, -3), (5, -7)$

✍ *Find the distance between each pair of points.*

25) $(5, -1), (2, -5)$

26) $(-4, -1), (0, 2)$

27) $(-4, 2), (2, 10)$

28) $(-1, -6), (4, 6)$

29) $(3, -2), (-6, -14)$

30) $(-3, 0), (1, 3)$

Answers

Find the slope of the line through each pair of points.

1) 2
2) 1

3) −4
4) 3

5) −1
6) 3

Sketch the graph of each line. (Using Slope–Intercept Form)

7)

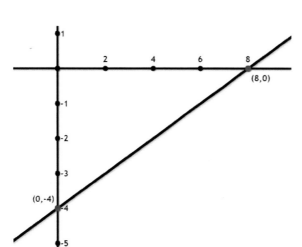

8)

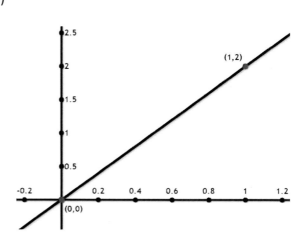

Sketch the graph of each line. (Graphing Lines Using Standard Form)

9) $y = 3x - 2$

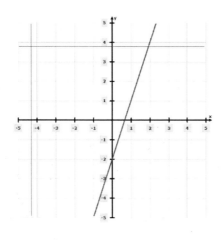

10) $y = -x + 1$

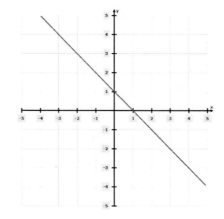

Write the equation of the line through the given points.

11) $y = 5x - 7$

12) $y = x + 3$

13) $y = 2x + 5$

14) $y = x - 1$

15) $y = -x + 5$

16) $y = 5x - 5$

Sketch the graph of each linear inequality. (Graphing Linear Inequalities)

17) $y > 3x - 1$

18) $y < -x + 4$

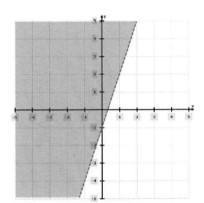

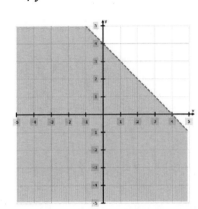

Find the midpoint of the line segment with the given endpoints.

19) $(-1, 0)$

20) $(1.5, 2.5)$

21) $(2, 1)$

22) $(-2, 4)$

23) $(5, -4)$

24) $(-1, -5)$

Find the distance between each pair of points.

25) 5

26) 5

27) 10

28) 13

29) 15

30) 5

Day 6:
Monomials and
Polynomials

Math Topics that you'll learn today:

- ✓ Writing Polynomials in Standard Form
- ✓ Simplifying Polynomials
- ✓ Adding and Subtracting Polynomials
- ✓ Multiplying Monomials
- ✓ Multiplying and Dividing Monomials
- ✓ Multiplying a Polynomial and a Monomial
- ✓ Multiplying Binomials
- ✓ Factoring Trinomials
- ✓ Operations with Polynomials

Mathematics is the supreme judge; from its decisions there is no appeal. ~Tobias Dantzig

Writing Polynomials in Standard Form

Step-by-step guide:

✓ A polynomial function $f(x)$ of degree n is of the form
$$f(x) = a_n x^n + a_{n-1} x_{n-1} + \cdots + a_1 x + a_0$$

✓ The first term is the one with the biggest power!

Examples:

1) Write this polynomial in standard form. $-12 + 3x^2 - 6x^4 =$

The first term is the one with the biggest power: $-12 + 3x^2 - 6x^4 = -6x^4 + 3x^2 - 12$

2) Write this polynomial in standard form. $5x^2 - 9x^5 + 8x^3 - 11 =$

The first term is the one with the biggest power: $5x^2 - 9x^5 + 8x^3 - 11 =$

$-9x^5 + 8x^3 + 5x^2 - 11$

Simplifying Polynomials

Step-by-step guide:

✓ Find "like" terms. (they have same variables with same power).

✓ Use "FOIL". (First-Out-In-Last) for binomials:
$$(x + a)(x + b) = x^2 + (b + a)x + ab$$

✓ Add or Subtract "like" terms using order of operation.

Examples:

1) Simplify this expression. $4x(6x - 3) =$

Use Distributive Property: $4x(6x - 3) = 24x^2 - 12x$

2) Simplify this expression. $(6x - 2)(2x - 3) =$

First apply FOIL method: $(a + b)(c + d) = ac + ad + bc + bd$

$(6x - 2)(2x - 3) = 12x^2 - 18x - 4x + 6$

Now combine like terms: $12x^2 - 18x - 4x + 6 = 12x^2 - 22x + 6$

Adding and Subtracting Polynomials

Step-by-step guide:

- ✓ Adding polynomials is just a matter of combining like terms, with some order of operations considerations thrown in.
- ✓ Be careful with the minus signs, and don't confuse addition and multiplication!

Examples:

1) Simplify the expressions. $(4x^3 + 3x^4) - (x^4 - 5x^3) =$

   First use Distributive Property for $-(x^4 - 5x^3)$, $\rightarrow -(x^4 - 5x^3) = -x^4 + 5x^3$

   $(4x^3 + 3x^4) - (x^4 - 5x^3) = 4x^3 + 3x^4 - x^4 + 5x^3$

   Now combine like terms: $4x^3 + 3x^4 - x^4 + 5x^3 = 2x^4 + 9x^3$

2) Add expressions. $(2x^3 - 6) + (9x^3 - 4x^2) =$

   Remove parentheses: $(2x^3 - 6) + (9x^3 - 4x^2) = 2x^3 - 6 + 9x^3 - 4x^2$

   Now combine like terms: $2x^3 - 6 + 9x^3 - 4x^2 = 11x^3 - 4x^2 - 6$

Multiplying Monomials

Step-by-step guide:

- ✓ A monomial is a polynomial with just one term, like $2x$ or $7y$.

Examples:

1) Multiply expressions. $5a^4b^3 \times 2a^3b^2 =$

   Use this formula: $x^a \times x^b = x^{a+b}$

   $a^4 \times a^3 = a^{4+3} = a^7$ and $b^3 \times b^2 = b^{3+2} = b^5$, Then: $5a^4b^3 \times 2a^3b^2 = 10a^7b^5$

2) Multiply expressions. $-4xy^4z^2 \times 3x^2y^5z^3 =$

   Use this formula: $x^a \times x^b = x^{a+b} \rightarrow x \times x^2 = x^{1+2} = x^3$, $y^4 \times y^5 = y^{4+5} = y^9$

   and $z^2 \times z^3 = z^{2+3} = z^5$, Then: $-4xy^4z^2 \times 3x^2y^5z^3 = -12x^3y^9z^5$

Multiplying and Dividing Monomials

Step-by-step guide:

- ✓ When you divide two monomials you need to divide their coefficients and then divide their variables.
- ✓ In case of exponents with the same base, you need to subtract their powers.
- ✓ Exponent's rules:

$$x^a \times x^b = x^{a+b} , \qquad \frac{x^a}{x^b} = x^{a-b}$$
$$\frac{1}{x^b} = x^{-b}, \quad (x^a)^b = x^{a \times b}$$
$$(xy)^a = x^a \times y^a$$

Examples:

1) Multiply expressions. $(-3x^7)(4x^3) =$
   Use this formula: $x^a \times x^b = x^{a+b} \rightarrow x^7 \times x^3 = x^{10}$
   Then: $(-3x^7)(4x^3) = -12x^{10}$

2) Dividing expressions. $\frac{18x^2y^5}{2xy^4} =$
   Use this formula: $\frac{x^a}{x^b} = x^{a-b}$, $\frac{x^2}{x} = x^{2-1} = x$ and $\frac{y^5}{y^4} = y^{5-4} = y$
   Then: $\frac{18x^2y^5}{2xy^4} = 9xy$

Multiplying a Polynomial and a Monomial

Step-by-step guide:

- ✓ When multiplying monomials, use the product rule for exponents.

- ✓ When multiplying a monomial by a polynomial, use the distributive property.

$$a \times (b + c) = a \times b + a \times c = ab = ac$$

Examples:

1) Multiply expressions. $-4x(5x + 9) =$

   Use Distributive Property: $-4x(5x + 9) = -20x^2 - 36x$

2) Multiply expressions. $2x(6x^2 - 3y^2) =$

   Use Distributive Property: $2x(6x^2 - 3y^2) = 12x^3 - 6xy^2$

Multiplying Binomials

Step-by-step guide:

✓ Use "FOIL". (First-Out-In-Last)
$$(x + a)(x + b) = x^2 + (b + a)x + ab$$

Examples:

1) Multiply Binomials. $(x - 2)(x + 2) =$

Use "FOIL". (First–Out–In–Last): $(x - 2)(x + 2) = x^2 + 2x - 2x - 4$

Then simplify: $x^2 + 2x - 2x - 4 = x^2 - 4$

2) Multiply Binomials. $(x + 5)(x - 2) =$

Use "FOIL". (First–Out–In–Last):

$(x + 5)(x - 2) = x^2 - 2x + 5x - 10$

Then simplify: $x^2 - 2x + 5x - 10 = x^2 + 3x - 10$

Factoring Trinomials

Step-by-step guide:

✓ "FOIL": $(x + a)(x + b) = x^2 + (b + a)x + ab$
✓ "Difference of Squares": $a^2 - b^2 = (a + b)(a - b)$
$$a^2 + 2ab + b^2 = (a + b)(a + b)$$
$$a^2 - 2ab + b^2 = (a - b)(a - b)$$
✓ "Reverse FOIL": $x^2 + (b + a)x + ab = (x + a)(x + b)$

Examples:

1) Factor this trinomial. $x^2 - 2x - 8 =$
Break the expression into groups: $(x^2 + 2x) + (-4x - 8)$
Now factor out x from $x^2 + 2x : x(x + 2)$ and factor out -4 from $-4x - 8: -4(x + 2)$
Then: $= x(x + 2) - 4(x + 2)$, now factor out like term: $x + 2$
Then: $(x + 2)(x - 4)$

2) Factor this trinomial. $x^2 - 6x + 8 =$

Break the expression into groups: $(x^2 - 2x) + (-4x + 8)$

Now factor out x from $x^2 - 2x$: $x(x - 2)$, and factor out -4 from $-4x + 8$: $-4(x - 2)$

Then: $= x(x - 2) - 4(x - 2)$, now factor out like term: $x - 2$

Then: $(x - 2)(x - 4)$

Operations with Polynomials

Step-by-step guide:

✓ When multiplying a monomial by a polynomial, use the distributive property.

$$a \times (b + c) = a \times b + a \times$$

Examples:

1) Multiply. $5(2x - 6) =$

Use the distributive property: $5(2x - 6) = 10x - 30$

2) Multiply. $2x(6x + 2) =$

Use the distributive property: $2x(6 + 2) = 12x^2 + 4x$

Day 6 Practices

✎ *Write each polynomial in standard form.*

1) $12x - 10x =$

2) $-3x - 3 + 14x - 11x =$

3) $5x^2 - 7x^3 =$

4) $3 + 4x^3 - 3 =$

5) $2x^2 + 1x - 6x^3 =$

6) $-x^2 + 2x^3 =$

✎ *Simplify each polynomial.*

7) $5(2x - 10) =$

8) $2x(4x - 2) =$

9) $4x(5x - 3) =$

10) $3x(7x + 3) =$

11) $4x(8x - 4) =$

12) $5x(5x + 4) =$

✎ *Add or subtract polynomials.*

13) $(-x^2 - 2) + (2x^2 + 1) =$

14) $(2x^2 + 3) - (3 - 4x^2) =$

15) $(2x^3 + 3x^2) - (x^3 + 8) =$

16) $(4x^3 - x^2) + (3x^2 - 5x) =$

17) $(7x^3 + 9x) - (3x^3 + 2) =$

18) $(2x^3 - 2) + (2x^3 + 2) =$

✎ *Simplify each expression. (Multiplying Monomials)*

19) $4u^7 \times (-2u^5) =$

20) $(-2p^7) \times (-3p^2) =$

21) $3xy^2z^3 \times 2z^2 =$

22) $5u^5t \times 3ut^2 =$

23) $(-9a^6) \times (-5a^2b^4) =$

24) $-2a^3b^2 \times 4a^2b =$

✎ *Simplify each expression. (Multiplying and Dividing Monomials)*

25) $(3x^7y^2)(16x^5y^4) =$

26) $(4x^4y^6)(7x^3y^4) =$

27) $(7x^2y^9)(12x^9y^{12}) =$

28) $\frac{12x^6y^8}{4x^4y^2} =$

29) $\frac{52x^9y^5}{4x^3y^4} =$

30) $\frac{80x^{12}y^9}{10x^6y^7} =$

✍ Find each product. (Multiplying a Polynomial and a Monomial)

31) $3x(9x + 2y) =$

32) $6x(x + 2y) =$

33) $9x(2x + 4y) =$

34) $12x(3x + 9) =$

35) $11x(2x - 11y) =$

36) $2x(6x - 6y) =$

✍ Find each product. (Multiplying Binomials)

37) $(x + 2)(x + 2) =$

38) $(x - 3)(x + 2) =$

39) $(x - 2)(x - 4) =$

40) $(x + 3)(x + 2) =$

41) $(x - 4)(x - 5) =$

42) $(x + 5)(x + 2) =$

✍ Factor each trinomial.

43) $x^2 + 8x + 15 =$

44) $x^2 - 5x + 6 =$

45) $x^2 + 6x + 8 =$

46) $x^2 - 8x + 16 =$

47) $x^2 - 7x + 12 =$

48) $x^2 + 11x + 18 =$

✍ Find each product. (Operations with Polynomials)

49) $9(6x + 2) =$

50) $8(3x + 7) =$

51) $5(6x - 1) =$

52) $-3(8x - 3) =$

53) $3x^2(6x - 5) =$

54) $5x^2(7x - 2) =$

Answers

1) $2x$
2) -3
3) $-7x^3 + 5x^2$

4) $4x^3$
5) $-6x^3 + 2x^2 + x$
6) $2x^3 - x^2$

7) $10x - 50$
8) $8x^2 - 4x$

9) $20x^2 - 12x$
10) $21x^2 + 9x$

11) $32x^2 - 16x$
12) $25x^2 + 20x$

13) $x^2 - 1$
14) $6x^2$
15) $x^3 + 3x^2 - 8$

16) $4x^3 + 2x^2 - 5x$
17) $4x^3 + 9x - 2$
18) $4x^3$

19) $-8u^{12}$
20) $6p^9$

21) $6xy^2z^5$
22) $15u^6t^3$

23) $45a^8b^4$
24) $-8a^5b^3$

25) $48x^{12}y^6$
26) $28x^7y^{10}$

27) $84x^{11}y^{21}$
28) $3x^2y^6$

29) $13x^6y$
30) $8x^6y^2$

31) $27x^2 + 6xy$
32) $6x^2 + 12xy$

33) $18x^2 + 36xy$
34) $36x^2 + 108x$

35) $22x^2 - 121xy$
36) $12x^2 - 12xy$

37) $x^2 + 4x + 4$
38) $x^2 - x - 6$

39) $x^2 - 6x + 8$
40) $x^2 + 5x + 6$

41) $x^2 - 9x + 20$
42) $x^2 + 7x + 10$

43) $(x + 3)(x + 5)$
44) $(x - 2)(x - 3)$

45) $(x + 4)(x + 2)$
46) $(x - 4)(x - 4)$

47) $(x - 3)(x - 4)$
48) $(x + 2)(x + 9)$

49) $54x + 18$
50) $24x + 56$
51) $30x - 5$

52) $-24x + 9$
53) $18x^3 - 15x^2$

54) $35x^3 - 10x^2$

Day 7:
Geometry and Statistics

Math Topics that you'll learn today:

- ✓ The Pythagorean Theorem
- ✓ Triangles
- ✓ Polygons
- ✓ Circles
- ✓ Trapezoids
- ✓ Cubes
- ✓ Rectangle Prisms
- ✓ Cylinder
- ✓ Mean, Median, Mode, and Range of the Given Data
- ✓ Bar Graph
- ✓ Box and Whisker Plots
- ✓ Stem– And– Leaf Plot
- ✓ Pie Graph
- ✓ Probability

Mathematics is like checkers in being suitable for the young, not too difficult, amusing, and without peril to the state. ~ Plato

The Pythagorean Theorem

Step-by-step guide:

- ✓ In any right triangle: $a^2 + b^2 = c^2$

Examples:

1) Find the missing length.

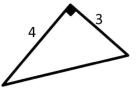

Use Pythagorean Theorem: $a^2 + b^2 = c^2$

Then: $a^2 + b^2 = c^2 \rightarrow 3^2 + 4^2 = c^2 \rightarrow 9 + 16 = c^2$

$c^2 = 25 \rightarrow c = 5$

2) Right triangle ABC has two legs of lengths 6 cm (AB) and 8 cm (AC). What is the length of the third side (BC)?

Use Pythagorean Theorem: $a^2 + b^2 = c^2$

Then: $a^2 + b^2 = c^2 \rightarrow 6^2 + 8^2 = c^2 \rightarrow 36 + 64 = c^2$

$c^2 = 100 \rightarrow c = 10$

Triangles

Step-by-step guide:

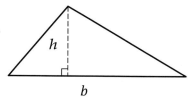

- ✓ In any triangle the sum of all angles is 180 degrees.
- ✓ Area of a triangle = $\frac{1}{2}$ ($base \times height$)

Examples:

What is the area of triangles?

1)

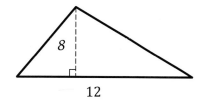

Solution:

Use the are formula: Area = $\frac{1}{2}$ ($base \times height$)

$base = 12$ and $height = 8$

Area = $\frac{1}{2}(12 \times 8) = \frac{1}{2}(96) = 48$

2)

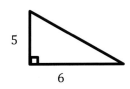

Solution:

Use the are formula: Area $= \frac{1}{2}(base \times height)$

$base = 6$ and $height = 5$

Area $= \frac{1}{2}(5 \times 6) = \frac{30}{2} = 15$

Polygons

Step-by-step guide:

Perimeter of a square $= 4 \times side = 4s$

Perimeter of a rectangle

$= 2(width + length)$

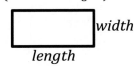

Perimeter of trapezoid

$= a + b + c + d$

Perimeter of a regular hexagon $= 6a$

Example: Find the perimeter of following regular hexagon.

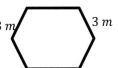

Perimeter of Pentagon $= 6a$

Perimeter of Pentagon $= 6a = 6 \times 3 = 18m$

Perimeter of a parallelogram $= 2(l + w)$

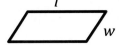

Circles

Step-by-step guide:

- ✓ In a circle, variable r is usually used for the radius and d for diameter and π is about 3.14.
- ✓ Area of a circle $= \pi r^2$
- ✓ Circumference of a circle $= 2\pi r$

Examples:

1) Find the area of the circle.

Use area formula: $Area = \pi r^2$,

$r = 4$ then: $Area = \pi(4)^2 = 16\pi$, $\pi = 3.14$ then:

$Area = 16 \times 3.14 = 50.24$

2) Find the Circumference of the circle.
   Use Circumference formula: $Circumference = 2\pi r$
   $r = 6$, then: $Circumference = 2\pi(6) = 12\pi$
   $\pi = 3.14$ then: $Circumference = 12 \times 3.14 = 37.68$
   $$(\pi = 3.14)$$

Trapezoids

Step-by-step guide:

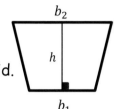

   ✓ A quadrilateral with at least one pair of parallel sides is a trapezoid.
   ✓ Area of a trapezoid $= \frac{1}{2}h(b_1 + b_2)$

Example:

Calculate the area of the trapezoid.

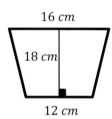

   Use area formula: $A = \frac{1}{2}h(b_1 + b_2)$

   $b_1 = 12$, $b_2 = 16$ and $h = 18$

   Then: $A = \frac{1}{2}18(12 + 16) = 9(28) = 252\ cm^2$

Cubes

Step-by-step guide:

   ✓ A cube is a three-dimensional solid object bounded by six square sides.
   ✓ Volume is the measure of the amount of space inside of a solid figure, like a cube, ball, cylinder or pyramid.
   ✓ Volume of a cube $= (one\ side)^3$
   ✓ surface area of cube $= 6 \times (one\ side)^2$

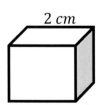

Example:

Find the volume and surface area of this cube.

   Use volume formula: $volume = (one\ side)^3$

   Then: $volume = (one\ side)^3 = (2)^3 = 8\ cm^3$

Use surface area formula: $surface\ area\ of\ cube: 6(one\ side)^2 = 6(2)^2 = 6(4) = 24\ cm^2$

Rectangular Prisms

Step-by-step guide:

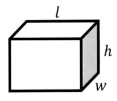

- ✓ A solid 3-dimensional object which has six rectangular faces.
- ✓ Volume of a Rectangular prism = **Length × Width × Height**

$Volume = l \times w \times h$ $Surface\ area = 2(wh + lw + lh)$

Example:

Find the volume and surface area of rectangular prism.

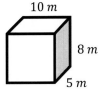

Use volume formula: $Volume = l \times w \times h$

Then: $Volume = 10 \times 5 \times 8 = 400\ m^3$

Use surface area formula: $Surface\ area = 2(wh + lw + lh)$

Then: $Surface\ area = 2(5 \times 8 + 10 \times 5 + 10 \times 8) = 2(40 + 50 + 80) = 340\ m^2$

Cylinder

Step-by-step guide:

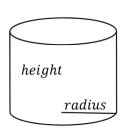

- ✓ A cylinder is a solid geometric figure with straight parallel sides and a circular or oval cross section.
- ✓ *Volume of Cylinder Formula* $= \pi(radius)^2 \times height\ (\pi = 3.14)$
- ✓ *Surface area of a cylinder* $= 2\pi r^2 + 2\pi rh$

Example:

Find the volume and Surface area of the follow Cylinder.

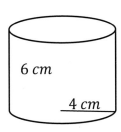

Use volume formula: $Volume = \pi(radius)^2 \times height$
Then: $Volume = \pi(4)^2 \times 6 = \pi 16 \times 6 = 96\pi$
$\pi = 3.14$ then: $Volume = 96\pi = 301.44$
Use surface area formula: $Surface\ area = 2\pi r^2 + 2\pi rh$
Then: $= 2\pi(4)^2 + 2\pi(4)(6) = 2\pi(16) + 2\pi(24) = 32\pi + 48\pi = 80\pi$
$\pi = 3.14$ then: $Surface\ area = 80 \times 3.14 = 251.2$

Mean, Median, Mode, and Range of the Given Data

Step-by-step guide:

- ✓ Mean: $\dfrac{\text{sum of the data}}{\text{total number of data entires}}$
- ✓ Mode: value in the list that appears most often
- ✓ Range: the difference of largest value and smallest value in the list

Examples:

1) What is the median of these numbers? $4, 9, 13, 8, 15, 18, 5$

   Write the numbers in order: $4, 5, 8, 9, 13, 15, 18$

   Median is the number in the middle. Therefore, the median is 9.

2) What is the mode of these numbers? $22, 16, 12, 9, 7, 6, 4, 6$

   Mode: value in the list that appears most often
   Therefore: mode is 6

Pie Graph

Step-by-step guide:

- ✓ A Pie Chart is a circle chart divided into sectors, each sector represents the relative size of each value.

Example:

A library has 840 books that include Mathematics, Physics, Chemistry, English and History. Use following graph to answer question.

What is the number of Mathematics books?

Number of total books = 840,
Percent of Mathematics books = 30% = 0.30
Then: $0.30 \times 840 = 252$

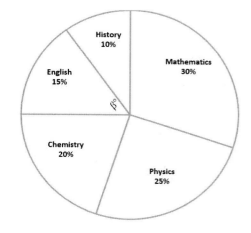

Probability Problems

Step-by-step guide:

- ✓ Probability is the likelihood of something happening in the future. It is expressed as a number between zero (can never happen) to 1 (will always happen).
- ✓ Probability can be expressed as a fraction, a decimal, or a percent.

Examples:

1) If there are 8 red balls and 12 blue balls in a basket, what is the probability that John will pick out a red ball from the basket?

   There are 8 red ball and 20 are total number of balls. Therefore, probability that John will pick out a red ball from the basket is 8 out of 20 or $\frac{8}{8+12} = \frac{8}{20} = \frac{2}{5}$.

2) A bag contains 18 balls: two green, five black, eight blue, a brown, a red and one white. If 17 balls are removed from the bag at random, what is the probability that a brown ball has been removed?

   If 17 balls are removed from the bag at random, there will be one ball in the bag.

   The probability of choosing a brown ball is 1 out of 18. Therefore, the probability of not choosing a brown ball is 17 out of 18 and the probability of having not a brown ball after removing 17 balls is the same.

Day 7 Practices

✍ *Find the missing side?*

1)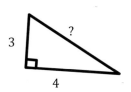

2)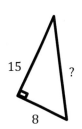

3)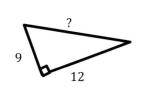

4)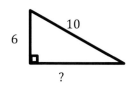

✍ *Find the measure of the unknown angle in each triangle.*

5)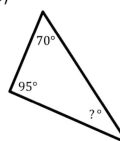

6)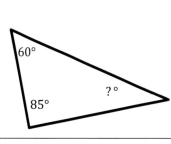

7)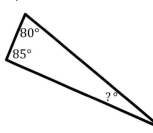

8)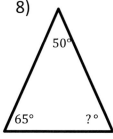

✍ *Find the perimeter of each shape.*

9)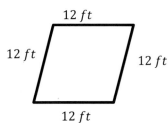

10)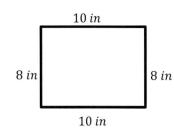

11)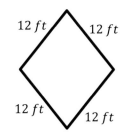

12)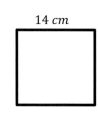

✍ *Complete the table below.* ($\pi = 3.14$)

13)

	Radius	Diameter	Circumference	Area
Circle 1	4 inches	8 inches	25.12 inches	50.24 square inches
Circle 2		12 meters		
Circle 3				12.56 square ft
Circle 4			18.84 miles	

Find the area of each trapezoid.

14)

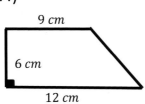

9 cm
6 cm
12 cm

15)

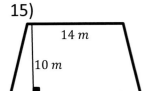

14 m
10 m
18 m

16)

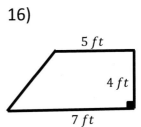

5 ft
4 ft
7 ft

17)

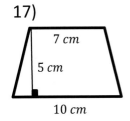

7 cm
5 cm
10 cm

 Find the volume of each cube.

18)

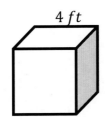

4 ft

19)

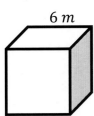

6 m

20)

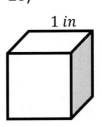

1 in

21)

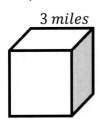

3 miles

 Find the volume of each Rectangular Prism.

22)

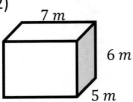

7 m
6 m
5 m

23)

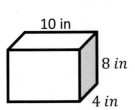

10 in
8 in
4 in

24)

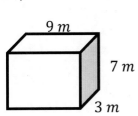

9 m
7 m
3 m

 Find the volume of each Cylinder. Round your answer to the nearest tenth. ($\pi = 3.14$)

25)

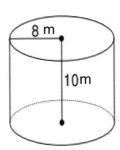

8 m
10m

26)

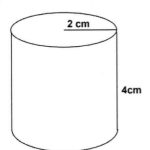

2 cm
4cm

27)

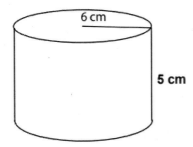

6 cm
5 cm

✍ *Solve.*

28) In a javelin throw competition, five athletics score 56, 58, 63, 57 and 61 meters. What are their Mean and Median? _____

✍ The circle graph below shows all Jason's expenses for last month. Jason spent $300 on his bills last month.

29) How much did Jason spend on his car last month? _____

30) How much did Jason spend for foods last month? _____

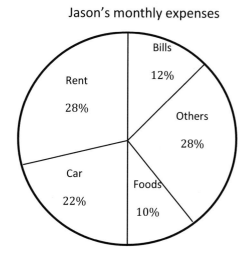

Jason's monthly expenses

Bills 12%

Others 28%

Rent 28%

Car 22%

Foods 10%

Solve.

31) Bag A contains 9 red marbles and 3 green marbles. Bag B contains 9 black marbles and 6 orange marbles. What is the probability of selecting a green marble at random from bag A? What is the probability of selecting a black marble at random from Bag B? _____ _____

Answers

1) 5

2) 17

3) 15

4) 8

5) 15°

6) 35°

7) 15°

8) 65°

9) 48 ft

10) 36 in

11) 48 ft

12) 56 cm

13)

	Radius	Diameter	Circumference	Area
Circle 1	4 inches	8 inches	25.12 inches	50.24 square inches
Circle 2	6 meters	12 meters	37.68 meters	113.04 meters
Circle 3	2 square ft	4 square ft	12.56 square ft	12.56 square ft
Circle 4	3 miles	6 miles	18.84 miles	28.26 miles

14) 63 cm^2

15) 160 m^2

16) 24 ft^2

17) 42.5 cm^2

18) 64 ft^3

19) 216 m^3

20) 1 in^3

21) 27 $miles^3$

22) 210 m^3

23) 320 in^3

24) 189 m^3

25) 2,009.6 m^3

26) 50.24 cm^3

27) 565.2 cm^3

28) $Mean: 59, Median: 58$

29) $550

30) $250

31) $\frac{1}{4}, \frac{3}{5}$

DAT Test Review

The Dental Admission Test (also known as the DAT) is a standardized test designed by the American Dental Association (ADA) to measure the general academic skills and perceptual ability of dental school applicants.

The DAT is comprised of multiple-choice test items consisting of four sections:

- ✓ Survey of the Natural Sciences
- ✓ Perceptual Ability
- ✓ Reading Comprehension
- ✓ Quantitative Reasoning

The Quantitative Reasoning section of the DAT measures applicants' math skills that will be required in dental schools. There are 40 multiple-choice questions test takers have 45 minutes to complete this section. A basic four function calculator on the computer screen will be available on this section.

In this book, there are five complete DAT Quantitative Reasoning Tests. Take these tests to see what score you'll be able to receive on a real DAT Quantitative Reasoning test.

Good luck!

Time to Test

Time to refine your quantitative reasoning skill with a practice test

Take a DAT Quantitative Reasoning test to simulate the test day experience. After you've finished, score your test using the answer keys.

Before You Start

- You'll need a pencil, a calculator and a timer to take the test.

- For each question, there are five possible answers. Choose which one is best.

- It's okay to guess. There is no penalty for wrong answers.

- Use the answer sheet provided to record your answers.

- After you've finished the test, review the answer key to see where you went wrong.

Good Luck!

DAT Quantitative Reasoning Practice Test 1

2019 - 2020

Total number of questions: 40

Total time: 45 Minutes

A basic four function calculator is permitted for DAT Quantitative Reasoning Test.

DAT Quantitative Reasoning Practice Tests Answer Sheet

Remove (or photocopy) this answer sheet and use it to complete the practice tests.

DAT Quantitative Reasoning Practice Test Answer Sheet

DAT Quantitative Reasoning Practice Test 1

1 Ⓐ Ⓑ Ⓒ Ⓓ Ⓔ	16 Ⓐ Ⓑ Ⓒ Ⓓ Ⓔ	31 Ⓐ Ⓑ Ⓒ Ⓓ Ⓔ
2 Ⓐ Ⓑ Ⓒ Ⓓ Ⓔ	17 Ⓐ Ⓑ Ⓒ Ⓓ Ⓔ	32 Ⓐ Ⓑ Ⓒ Ⓓ Ⓔ
3 Ⓐ Ⓑ Ⓒ Ⓓ Ⓔ	18 Ⓐ Ⓑ Ⓒ Ⓓ Ⓔ	33 Ⓐ Ⓑ Ⓒ Ⓓ Ⓔ
4 Ⓐ Ⓑ Ⓒ Ⓓ Ⓔ	19 Ⓐ Ⓑ Ⓒ Ⓓ Ⓔ	34 Ⓐ Ⓑ Ⓒ Ⓓ Ⓔ
5 Ⓐ Ⓑ Ⓒ Ⓓ Ⓔ	20 Ⓐ Ⓑ Ⓒ Ⓓ Ⓔ	35 Ⓐ Ⓑ Ⓒ Ⓓ Ⓔ
6 Ⓐ Ⓑ Ⓒ Ⓓ Ⓔ	21 Ⓐ Ⓑ Ⓒ Ⓓ Ⓔ	36 Ⓐ Ⓑ Ⓒ Ⓓ Ⓔ
7 Ⓐ Ⓑ Ⓒ Ⓓ Ⓔ	22 Ⓐ Ⓑ Ⓒ Ⓓ Ⓔ	37 Ⓐ Ⓑ Ⓒ Ⓓ Ⓔ
8 Ⓐ Ⓑ Ⓒ Ⓓ Ⓔ	23 Ⓐ Ⓑ Ⓒ Ⓓ Ⓔ	38 Ⓐ Ⓑ Ⓒ Ⓓ Ⓔ
9 Ⓐ Ⓑ Ⓒ Ⓓ Ⓔ	24 Ⓐ Ⓑ Ⓒ Ⓓ Ⓔ	39 Ⓐ Ⓑ Ⓒ Ⓓ Ⓔ
10 Ⓐ Ⓑ Ⓒ Ⓓ Ⓔ	25 Ⓐ Ⓑ Ⓒ Ⓓ Ⓔ	40 Ⓐ Ⓑ Ⓒ Ⓓ Ⓔ
11 Ⓐ Ⓑ Ⓒ Ⓓ Ⓔ	26 Ⓐ Ⓑ Ⓒ Ⓓ Ⓔ	
12 Ⓐ Ⓑ Ⓒ Ⓓ Ⓔ	27 Ⓐ Ⓑ Ⓒ Ⓓ Ⓔ	
13 Ⓐ Ⓑ Ⓒ Ⓓ Ⓔ	28 Ⓐ Ⓑ Ⓒ Ⓓ Ⓔ	
14 Ⓐ Ⓑ Ⓒ Ⓓ Ⓔ	29 Ⓐ Ⓑ Ⓒ Ⓓ Ⓔ	
15 Ⓐ Ⓑ Ⓒ Ⓓ Ⓔ	30 Ⓐ Ⓑ Ⓒ Ⓓ Ⓔ	

1) When a number is subtracted from 24 and the difference is divided by that number, the result is 3. What is the value of the number?
   A. 2
   B. 4
   C. 6
   D. 12
   E. 24

2) An angle is equal to one fifth of its supplement. What is the measure of that angle?
   A. 20
   B. 30
   C. 45
   D. 60
   E. 90

3) John traveled 150 km in 6 hours and Alice traveled 180 km in 4 hours. What is the ratio of the average speed of John to average speed of Alice?
   A. $3 : 2$
   B. $2 : 3$
   C. $5 : 9$
   D. $5 : 6$
   E. $11 : 16$

4) If 40% of a class are girls, and 35% of girls play tennis, what percent of the class play tennis?
   A. 10%
   B. 14%
   C. 20%
   D. 40%
   E. 80%

5) In five successive hours, a car traveled 40 km, 45 km, 50 km, 35 km and 55 km. In the next five hours, it traveled with an average speed of 50 $km\ per\ hour$. Find the total distance the car traveled in 10 hours.
   A. 425 km
   B. 450 km
   C. 475 km
   D. 500 km
   E. 1,000 km

6) How long does a 420−miles trip take moving at 50 miles per hour (*mph*)?
   A. 4 *hours*
   B. 6 *hours and* 24 *minutes*
   C. 8 *hours and* 24 *minutes*
   D. 8 *hours and* 30 *minutes*
   E. 10 *hours and* 30 *minutes*

7) Right triangle *ABC* has two legs of lengths 6 *cm* (*AB*) and 8 *cm* (*AC*). What is the length of the third side (*BC*)?
   A. 4 *cm*
   B. 6 *cm*
   C. 8 *cm*
   D. 10 *cm*
   E. 20 *cm*

8) The ratio of boys to girls in a school is 2: 3. If there are 600 students in a school, how many boys are in the school.
   A. 540
   B. 360
   C. 300
   D. 280
   E. 240

9) 25 is What percent of 20?
   A. 20%
   B. 25%
   C. 125%
   D. 150%
   E. 300%

10) The perimeter of the trapezoid below is 54. What is its area?
   A. 252 cm^2
   B. 234 cm^2
   C. 216 cm^2
   D. 154 cm^2
   E. 130cm^2

18 cm

12 cm   14 cm

11) Two third of 18 is equal to $\frac{2}{5}$ of what number?
    A. 12
    B. 20
    C. 30
    D. 60
    E. 90

12) The marked price of a computer is D dollar. Its price decreased by 20% in January and later increased by 10% in February. What is the final price of the computer in D dollar?
    A. 0.80 D
    B. 0.88 D
    C. 0.90 D
    D. 1.20 D
    E. 1.40 D

13) The area of a circle is 25 π. What is the circumference of the circle?
    A. 5 π
    B. 10 π
    C. 32 π
    D. 64 π
    E. 124 π

14) In 1999, the average worker's income increased $3,000 per year starting from $24,000 annual salary. Which equation represents income greater than average? (I = income, x = number of years after 1999)
    A. $I > 3000\,x + 24000$
    B. $I > -3000\,x + 24000$
    C. $I < -3000\,x + 24000$
    D. $I < 3000\,x - 24000$
    E. $I < 24{,}000\,x + 24000$

15) From last year, the price of gasoline has increased from $1.25 per gallon to $1.75 per gallon. The new price is what percent of the original price?
    A. 72%
    B. 120%
    C. 140%
    D. 160%
    E. 180%

16) A boat sails 40 miles south and then 30 miles east. How far is the boat from its start point?
   A. 45 *miles*
   B. 50 *miles*
   C. 60 *miles*
   D. 70 *miles*
   E. 80 *miles*

17) Sophia purchased a sofa for $530.40. The sofa is regularly priced at $624. What was the percent discount Sophia received on the sofa?
   A. 12%
   B. 15%
   C. 20%
   D. 25%
   E. 40%

18) The score of Emma was half as that of Ava and the score of Mia was twice that of Ava. If the score of Mia was 60, what is the score of Emma?
   A. 12
   B. 15
   C. 20
   D. 30
   E. 40

19) The average of five consecutive numbers is 38. What is the smallest number?
   A. 38
   B. 36
   C. 34
   D. 12
   E. 8

20) How many tiles of $8\ cm^2$ is needed to cover a floor of dimension $6\ cm$ by $24\ cm$?
   A. 6
   B. 12
   C. 18
   D. 24

   E. 36
21) A rope weighs 600 grams per meter of length. What is the weight in kilograms of 12.2 meters of this rope? ($1\ kilograms\ =\ 1000\ grams$)
   A. 0.0732
   B. 0.732
   C. 7.32
   D. 7,320
   E. 73,200

22) A chemical solution contains 4% alcohol. If there is $24\ ml$ of alcohol, what is the volume of the solution?
   A. $240\ ml$
   B. $480\ ml$
   C. $600\ ml$
   D. $1,200\ ml$
   E. $2,400\ ml$

23) The average weight of 18 girls in a class is $60\ kg$ and the average weight of 32 boys in the same class is $62\ kg$. What is the average weight of all the 50 students in that class?
   A. 60
   B. 61.28
   C. 61.68
   D. 61.90
   E. 62.20

24) The price of a laptop is decreased by 10% to $360. What is its original price?
   A. $320
   B. $380
   C. $400
   D. $450
   E. $500

25) The radius of the following cylinder is 8 inches and its height is 12 inches. What is the surface area of the cylinder?
   A. $64\ \pi\ in^2$
   B. $128\ \pi\ in^2$
   C. $192\ \pi\ in^2$
   D. $256\ \pi\ in^2$
   E. $320\ \pi\ in^2$

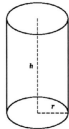

26) The average of $13, 15, 20$ and x is 18. What is the value of x?
   A. 9
   B. 15
   C. 18
   D. 20
   E. 24

27) The price of a sofa is decreased by 25% to $420. What was its original price?
   A. $480
   B. $520
   C. $560
   D. $600
   E. $800

28) A bank is offering 4.5% simple interest on a savings account. If you deposit $8,000, how much interest will you earn in five years?
   A. $360
   B. $720
   C. $1,800
   D. $3,600
   E. $4,800

29) Multiply and write the product in scientific notation:

$$(4.2 \times 10^6) \times (2.6 \times 10^{-5})$$

   A. 1092×10
   B. 10.92×10^6
   C. 109.2×10^{-5}
   D. 10.92×10^{11}
   E. 1.092×10^2

30) If the height of a right pyramid is $12\ cm$ and its base is a square with side $6\ cm$. What is its volume?
   A. $32\ cm^3$
   B. $36\ cm^3$
   C. $48\ cm^3$
   D. $72\ cm^3$
   E. $144\ cm^3$

31) Solve for x: $4(x + 1) = 6(x - 4) + 20$
   A. 12
   B. 8
   C. 6.2
   D. 5.5
   E. 4

32) Which of the following expressions is equivalent to

$$2x\,(4 + 2y)?$$

   A. $2xy + 8x$
   B. $8xy + 8x$
   C. $xy + 8$
   D. $2xy + 8x$
   E. $4xy + 8x$

33) If $y = 4ab + 3b^3$, what is y when $a = 2$ and $b = 3$?
    A. 24
    B. 31
    C. 36
    D. 51
    E. 105

34) 11 yards 6 feet and 4 inches equals to how many inches?
    A. 388
    B. 468
    C. 472
    D. 476
    E. 486

35) 5 less than twice a positive integer is 83. What is the integer?
    A. 39
    B. 41
    C. 42
    D. 44
    E. 50

36) A shirt costing $200 is discounted 15%. After a month, the shirt is discounted another 15%. Which of the following expressions can be used to find the selling price of the shirt?
    A. $(200)(0.70)$
    B. $(200) - 200(0.30)$
    C. $(200)(0.15) - (200)(0.15)$
    D. $(200)(0.85)(0.85)$
    E. $(200)(0.85)(0.85) - (200)(0.15)$

37) Which of the following points lies on the line $2x + 4y = 10$
    A. $(2, 1)$
    B. $(-1, 3)$
    C. $(-2, 2)$
    D. $(2, 2)$
    E. $(2, 8)$

38) The price of a car was $20,000 in 2014, $16,000 in 2015 and $12,800 in 2016. What is the rate of depreciation of the price of car per year?
    A. 15%
    B. 20%
    C. 25%
    D. 30%
    E. 50%

39) A ladder leans against a wall forming a $60°$ angle between the ground and the ladder. If the bottom of the ladder is 30 feet away from the wall, how long is the ladder?
   A. $30\ feet$
   B. $40\ feet$
   C. $50\ feet$
   D. $60\ feet$
   E. $120\ feet$

40) Right triangle ABC is shown below. Which of the following is true for all possible values of angle A and B?

A. $tan\ A\ =\ tan\ B$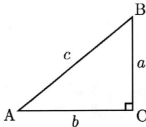

B. $sin\ A\ =\ cos\ B$

C. $tan^2 A = tan^2 B$

D. $tan\ A = 1$

E. $cot\ A = sinB$

End of DAT Quantitative Reasoning Practice Test 1

DAT Quantitative Reasoning Practice Test 2

2019 - 2020

Total number of questions: 40

Total time: 45 Minutes

A basic four function calculator is permitted for DAT Quantitative Reasoning Test.

DAT Quantitative Reasoning Practice Tests Answer Sheet

Remove (or photocopy) this answer sheet and use it to complete the practice tests.

DAT Quantitative Reasoning Practice Test Answer Sheet

DAT Quantitative Reasoning Practice Test 2

1	Ⓐ Ⓑ Ⓒ Ⓓ Ⓔ	16	Ⓐ Ⓑ Ⓒ Ⓓ Ⓔ	31 Ⓐ Ⓑ Ⓒ Ⓓ Ⓔ
2	Ⓐ Ⓑ Ⓒ Ⓓ Ⓔ	17	Ⓐ Ⓑ Ⓒ Ⓓ Ⓔ	32 Ⓐ Ⓑ Ⓒ Ⓓ Ⓔ
3	Ⓐ Ⓑ Ⓒ Ⓓ Ⓔ	18	Ⓐ Ⓑ Ⓒ Ⓓ Ⓔ	33 Ⓐ Ⓑ Ⓒ Ⓓ Ⓔ
4	Ⓐ Ⓑ Ⓒ Ⓓ Ⓔ	19	Ⓐ Ⓑ Ⓒ Ⓓ Ⓔ	34 Ⓐ Ⓑ Ⓒ Ⓓ Ⓔ
5	Ⓐ Ⓑ Ⓒ Ⓓ Ⓔ	20	Ⓐ Ⓑ Ⓒ Ⓓ Ⓔ	35 Ⓐ Ⓑ Ⓒ Ⓓ Ⓔ
6	Ⓐ Ⓑ Ⓒ Ⓓ Ⓔ	21	Ⓐ Ⓑ Ⓒ Ⓓ Ⓔ	36 Ⓐ Ⓑ Ⓒ Ⓓ Ⓔ
7	Ⓐ Ⓑ Ⓒ Ⓓ Ⓔ	22	Ⓐ Ⓑ Ⓒ Ⓓ Ⓔ	37 Ⓐ Ⓑ Ⓒ Ⓓ Ⓔ
8	Ⓐ Ⓑ Ⓒ Ⓓ Ⓔ	23	Ⓐ Ⓑ Ⓒ Ⓓ Ⓔ	38 Ⓐ Ⓑ Ⓒ Ⓓ Ⓔ
9	Ⓐ Ⓑ Ⓒ Ⓓ Ⓔ	24	Ⓐ Ⓑ Ⓒ Ⓓ Ⓔ	39 Ⓐ Ⓑ Ⓒ Ⓓ Ⓔ
10	Ⓐ Ⓑ Ⓒ Ⓓ Ⓔ	25	Ⓐ Ⓑ Ⓒ Ⓓ Ⓔ	40 Ⓐ Ⓑ Ⓒ Ⓓ Ⓔ
11	Ⓐ Ⓑ Ⓒ Ⓓ Ⓔ	26	Ⓐ Ⓑ Ⓒ Ⓓ Ⓔ	
12	Ⓐ Ⓑ Ⓒ Ⓓ Ⓔ	27	Ⓐ Ⓑ Ⓒ Ⓓ Ⓔ	
13	Ⓐ Ⓑ Ⓒ Ⓓ Ⓔ	28	Ⓐ Ⓑ Ⓒ Ⓓ Ⓔ	
14	Ⓐ Ⓑ Ⓒ Ⓓ Ⓔ	29	Ⓐ Ⓑ Ⓒ Ⓓ Ⓔ	
15	Ⓐ Ⓑ Ⓒ Ⓓ Ⓔ	30	Ⓐ Ⓑ Ⓒ Ⓓ Ⓔ	

1) If $f(x) = 3x^3 + 5x^2 + 2x$ and $g(x) = -2$, what is the value of $f(g(x))$?
    A. 36
    B. 32
    C. 24
    D. 8
    E. -8

2) The diagonal of a rectangle is 10 inches long and the height of the rectangle is 8 inches. What is the perimeter of the rectangle?
    A. 10 *inches*
    B. 12 *inches*
    C. 16 *inches*
    D. 18 *inches*
    E. 28 *inches*

3) If $x = \frac{1}{3}$ and $y = \frac{9}{21}$, then which is equal to $\frac{1}{x} \div \frac{y}{3}$?
    A. $\frac{1}{7}$
    B. $\frac{1}{21}$
    C. $\frac{1}{3}$
    D. 9
    E. 21

4) The mean of 50 test scores was calculated as 85. But, it turned out that one of the scores was misread as 94 but it was 69. What is the mean?
    A. 84.5
    B. 87
    C. 87.5
    D. 88.5
    E. 90.5

5) Which of the following answers represents the compound inequality $-4 \leq 4x - 8 < 16$?
    A. $-2 \leq x \leq 8$
    B. $-2 < x \leq 8$
    C. $1 < x \leq 6$
    D. $1 \leq x < 6$
    E. $2 \leq x \leq 6$

6) A swimming pool holds 2,000 cubic feet of water. The swimming pool is 25 feet long and 10 feet wide. How deep is the swimming pool?
    A. 2 *feet*
    B. 4 *feet*
    C. 6 *feet*
    D. 7 *feet*
    E. 8 *feet*

7) Mr. Carlos family are choosing a menu for their reception. They have 3 choices of appetizers, 7 choices of entrees, 4 choices of cake. How many different menu combinations are possible for them to choose?
    A. 12
    B. 32
    C. 84
    D. 120
    E. 240

8) What is the area of a square whose diagonal is 8?
    A. 16
    B. 32
    C. 36
    D. 64
    E. 124

9) The perimeter of a rectangular yard is 60 meters. What is its length if its width is twice its length?
    A. 10 *meters*
    B. 18 *meters*
    C. 20 *meters*
    D. 24 *meters*
    E. 36 *meters*

10) The average of 6 numbers is 12. The average of 4 of those numbers is 10. What is the average of the other two numbers?
    A. 10
    B. 12
    C. 14
    D. 16
    E. 24

11) The average of five numbers is 24. If a sixth number 42 is added, then, what is the new average?
    A. 25
    B. 26
    C. 27
    D. 28
    E. 36

12) The ratio of boys and girls in a class is 4 : 7. If there are 66 students in the class, how many more boys should be enrolled to make the ratio 1 : 1?

    A. 8

    B. 10

    C. 12

    D. 18

    E. 28

13) Jason needs an 76% average in his writing class to pass. On his first 4 exams, he earned scores of 68%, 72%, 85%, and 90%. What is the minimum score Jason can earn on his fifth and final test to pass?

    A. 80%,

    B. 70%

    C. 68%

    D. 65%

    E. 60%

14) 5 less than twice a positive integer is 53. What is the integer?

    A. 29

    B. 41

    C. 42

    D. 44

    E. 53

15) A bank is offering 3.5% simple interest on a savings account. If you deposit $12,000, how much interest will you earn in two years?

    A. $420

    B. $840

    C. $4,200

    D. $8,400

    E. $9,600

16) Simplify $6x^2y^3(2x^2y)^3 =$

    A. $12x^4y^6$

    B. $12x^8y^6$

    C. $48x^4y^6$

    D. $48x^8y^6$

    E. $96x^8y^6$

17) The radius of a cylinder is 6 inches and its height is 12 inches. What is the surface area of the cylinder in square inches?

A. 567.98
B. 640
C. 678.24
D. 888.25
E. 910.21

18) A cruise line ship left Port A and traveled 80 miles due west and then 150 miles due north. At this point, what is the shortest distance from the cruise to port A?
A. 70 $miles$
B. 80 $miles$
C. 150 $miles$
D. 230 $miles$
E. 170 $miles$

19) What is the equivalent temperature of $140°F$ in Celsius?

$$C = \frac{5}{9}(F - 32)$$

A. 32
B. 40
C. 48
D. 52
E. 60

20) If 150% of a number is 75, then what is the 95% of that number?
A. 47.5
B. 50
C. 70
D. 85
E. 90

21) In two successive years, the population of a town is increased by 15% and 20%. What percent of the population is increased after two years?
A. 32%
B. 35%
C. 38%
D. 68%
E. 70%

22) Last week 24,000 fans attended a football match. This week three times as many bought tickets, but one sixth of them cancelled their tickets. How many are attending this week?
    A. 48,000
    B. 54,000
    C. 60,000
    D. 72,000
    E. 84,000

23) What is the perimeter of a square that has an area of 64 square inches?
    A. 144 *inches*
    B. 64 *inches*
    C. 56 *inches*
    D. 48 *inches*
    E. 32 *inches*

24) In the xy-plane, the point (4,3) and (3,2) are on line A. Which of the following points could also be on line A?
    A. $(-1,2)$
    B. $(5,7)$
    C. $(3,4)$
    D. $(-1,-2)$
    E. $(-7,-9)$

25) If $f(x) = 2x^3 + 5x^2 + 2x$ and $g(x) = -2$, what is the value of $f(g(x))$?
    A. 36
    B. 32
    C. 24
    D. 4
    E. 0

26) The area of a circle is 64π. What is the diameter of the circle?
    A. 4
    B. 8
    C. 12
    D. 14
    E. 16

27) If a tree casts a 22–foot shadow at the same time that a 3 feet yardstick casts a 2–foot shadow, what is the height of the tree?

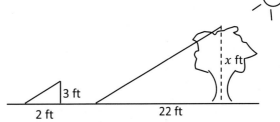

A. 24 ft
B. 28 ft
C. 33 ft
D. 98 ft
E. 108 ft

28) Which of the following is equal to the expression below?

$$(4x + 2y)(2x - y)$$

A. $8x^2 - 2y^2$
B. $2x^2 + 6xy - 2y^2$
C. $24x^2 + 2xy - 2y^2$
D. $8x^2 + 2xy - 2y^2$
E. $8x^2 + 2xy - 2y^2$

29) What is the product of all possible values of x in the following equation?

$$|x - 10| = 3$$

A. 3
B. 7
C. 13
D. 91
E. 100

30) What is the slope of a line that is perpendicular to the line
$$4x - 2y = 12?$$

A. -2
B. $-\dfrac{1}{2}$
C. 4
D. 12
E. 14

31) What is the value of the expression $5(x - 2y) + (2 - x)^2$ when $x = 3$ and $= -2$?
A. -4
B. 20
C. 36
D. 50
E. 80

32) Jason is 15 miles ahead of Joe running at 5.5 miles per hour and Joe is running at the speed of 7 miles per hour. How long does it take Joe to catch Jason?
   A. 3 *hours*
   B. 4 *hours*
   C. 6 *hours*
   D. 8 *hours*
   E. 10 *hours*

33) 88 students took an exam and 11 of them failed. What percent of the students passed the exam?
   A. 20%
   B. 40.3%
   C. 60%
   D. 87.5%
   E. 90.15

34) If $tan\ \theta = \frac{5}{12}$ and $sin\ \theta > 0$, then $cos\ \theta = ?$
   A. $-\frac{5}{13}$
   B. $\frac{12}{13}$
   C. $\frac{13}{12}$
   D. $-\frac{12}{13}$
   E. 0

35) If the area of trapezoid is 100, what is the perimeter of the trapezoid?

   A. 25

   B. 35

   C. 45

   D. 55

   E. 65

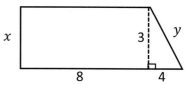

36) A number is chosen at random from 1 to 25. Find the probability of not selecting a composite number.

    A. $\frac{1}{25}$

    B. 25

    C. $\frac{2}{5}$

    D. 1

    E. 0

37) Removing which of the following numbers will change the average of the numbers to 6?
                        1, 4, 5, 8, 11, 12

    A. 1

    B. 4

    C. 5

    D. 11

    E. 12

38) If $(x - 2)^2 + 1 > 3x - 1$, then x can equal which of the following?

    A. 1

    B. 6

    C. 8

    D. 3

    E. 4

39) If 150% of a number is 75, then what is 90% of that number?

    A. 45

    B. 50

    C. 70

    D. 85

    E. 90

40) If one angle of a right triangle measures 60°, what is the sine of the other acute angle?

    A. $\frac{1}{2}$

    B. $\frac{\sqrt{2}}{2}$

    C. $\frac{\sqrt{3}}{2}$

    D. 1

    E. $\sqrt{3}$

End of DAT Quantitative Reasoning Practice Test 2

DAT Quantitative Reasoning Practice Tests
Answers and Explanations

Now, it's time to review your results to see where you went wrong and what areas you need to improve.

DAT Quantitative Reasoning Practice Test 1				DAT Quantitative Reasoning Practice Test 2			
1	C	21	C	1	E	21	C
2	B	22	C	2	E	22	C
3	C	23	B	3	C	23	E
4	B	24	C	4	A	24	D
5	C	25	E	5	D	25	E
6	C	26	E	6	E	26	E
7	D	27	C	7	C	27	C
8	E	28	C	8	B	28	A
9	C	29	E	9	A	29	D
10	E	30	E	10	D	30	B
11	C	31	E	11	C	31	C
12	B	32	E	12	D	32	E
13	B	33	E	13	D	33	D
14	A	34	C	14	A	34	B
15	C	35	D	15	B	35	B
16	B	36	D	16	E	36	C
17	B	37	B	17	C	37	D
18	B	38	B	18	E	38	A
19	B	39	D	19	E	39	C
20	C	40	B	20	A	40	A

DAT Quantitative Reasoning Practice Test 1

1) Choice C is correct

Let x be the number. Write the equation and solve for x.$(24 - x) \div x = 3$. Multiply both sides by x. $(24 - x) = 3x$, then add x both sides. $24 = 4x$, now divide both sides by 4.

$x = 6$

2) Choice B is correct

The sum of supplement angles is 180. Let x be that angle. Therefore, $x + 5x = 180$

$6x = 180$, divide both sides by 6: $x = 30$

3) Choice C is correct

The average speed of john is: $150 \div 6 = 25$, The average speed of Alice is: $180 \div 4 = 45$

Write the ratio and simplify. $25 : 45 \Rightarrow 5 : 9$

4) Choice B is correct

The percent of girls playing tennis is: $40\% \times 35\% = 0.40 \times 0.35 = 0.14 = 14\%$

5) Choice C is correct

Add the first 5 numbers. $40 + 45 + 50 + 35 + 55 = 225$

To find the distance traveled in the next 5 hours, multiply the average by number of hours.

$Distance = Average \times Rate = 50 \times 5 = 250$, Add both numbers. $250 + 225 = 475$

6) Choice C is correct

Use distance formula: $Distance = Rate \times time \Rightarrow 420 = 50 \times T$, divide both sides by 50. $420 \div 50 = T \Rightarrow T = 8.4 \ hours$.Change hours to minutes for the decimal part. $0.4 \ hours = 0.4 \times 60 = 24 \ minutes$.

7) Choice D is correct

Use Pythagorean Theorem: $a^2 + b^2 = c^2$, $6^2 + 8^2 = c^2 \Rightarrow 100 = c^2 \Rightarrow c = 10$

8) Choice E is correct

Th ratio of boy to girls is $2 : 3$. Therefore, there are 2 boys out of 5 students. To find the answer, first divide the total number of students by 5, then multiply the result by 2.

$600 \div 5 = 120 \Rightarrow 120 \times 2 = 240$

9) Choice C is correct

Use percent formula:part $= \frac{percent}{100} \times$ whole

$25 = \frac{percent}{100} \times 20 \Rightarrow 25 = \frac{percent \times 20}{100} \Rightarrow 25$
$= \frac{percent \times 2}{10}$, *multiply both sides by* 10.
$250 = percent \times 2$, divide both sides by 2. $125 = percent$

10) Choice E is correct

The perimeter of the trapezoid is 54.

Therefore, the missing side (height) is = $54 - 18 - 12 - 14 = 10$

Area of the trapezoid: $A = \frac{1}{2} h (b_1 + b_2) = \frac{1}{2} (10) (12 + 14) = 130$

11) Choice C is correct

Let x be the number. Write the equation and solve for x.

$\frac{2}{3} \times 18 = \frac{2}{5} . x \Rightarrow \frac{2 \times 18}{3} = \frac{2x}{5}$, use cross multiplication to solve for x.

$5 \times 36 = 2x \times 3 \Rightarrow 180 = 6x \Rightarrow x = 30$

12) Choice B is correct

To find the discount, multiply the number by $(100\% - rate\ of\ discount)$.

Therefore, for the first discount we get: $(D) (100\% - 20\%) = (D) (0.80) = 0.80\ D$

For increase of 10%: $(0.80\ D)(100\% + 10\%) = (0.80\ D)(1.10) = 0.88\ D = 88\%\ of\ D$

13) Choice B is correct

Use the formula of areas of circles. $Area = \pi r^2 \Rightarrow 25\ \pi = \pi r^2 \Rightarrow 25 = r^2 \Rightarrow r = 5$

Radius of the circle is 5. Now, use the circumference formula: Circumference $= 2\pi r = 2\pi (5) = 10\ \pi$

14) Choice A is correct

Let x be the number of years. Therefore, \$3,000 per year equals $2000x$. starting from \$24,000 annual salary means you should add that amount to $3000x$. Income more than that is:

$I > 3000\ x + 24000$

15) Choice C is correct

The question is this: 1.75 is what percent of 1.25? Use percent formula:

$$\text{part} = \frac{\text{percent}}{100} \times \text{whole}$$

$$1.75 = \frac{percent}{100} \times 1.25 \Rightarrow 1.75 = \frac{percent \times 1.25}{100} \Rightarrow 175 = percent \times 1.25$$

$$\Rightarrow percent = \frac{175}{1.25} = 140$$

16) Choice B is correct

Use the information provided in the question to draw the shape.

Use Pythagorean Theorem: $a^2 + b^2 = c^2$

$$40^2 + 30^2 = c^2 \Rightarrow 1600 + 900 = c^2 \Rightarrow 2500 = c^2 \Rightarrow c = 50$$

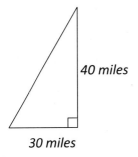

40 miles

30 miles

17) Choice B is correct

The question is this: 530.40 is what percent of 624?

Use percent formula: $\text{part} = \frac{\text{percent}}{100} \times \text{whole}$

$$530.40 = \frac{percent}{100} \times 624 \Rightarrow 530.40 = \frac{percent \times 624}{100} \Rightarrow 53040 = percent \times 624 \Rightarrow$$

$$percent = \frac{53040}{624} = 85$$

530.40 is 85% of 624. Therefore, the discount is: $100\% - 85\% = 15\%$

18) Choice B is correct

If the score of Mia was 60, therefore the score of Ava is 30. Since, the score of Emma was half as that of Ava, therefore, the score of Emma is 15.

19) Choice B is correct

Let x be the smallest number. Then, these are the numbers: $x, x + 1, x + 2, x + 3, x + 4$

$$average = \frac{\text{sum of terms}}{\text{number of terms}} \Rightarrow 38 = \frac{x+(x+1)+(x+2)+(x+3)+(x+4)}{5} \Rightarrow 38 = \frac{5x+10}{5} \Rightarrow 190 = 5x +$$
$$10 \Rightarrow 180 = 5x \Rightarrow x = 36$$

20) Choice C is correct

The area of the floor is: $6 \, cm \times 24 \, cm = 144 \, cm^2$, The number is tiles needed $= 144 \div 8 = 18$

21) Choice C is correct

The weight of 12.2 meters of this rope is: $12.2 \times 600 \, g = 7320 \, g$,

$1 \, kg = 1000 \, g$, therefore, $7320 \, g \div 1000 = 7.32 \, kg$

22) Choice C is correct

4% of the volume of the solution is alcohol. Let x be the volume of the solution.

Then: $4\% \ of \ x = 24 \ ml \Rightarrow 0.04 \ x = 24 \Rightarrow x = 24 \div 0.04 = 600$

23) Choice B is correct

$average = \frac{sum \ of \ terms}{number \ of \ terms}$, The sum of the weight of all girls is: $18 \times 60 = 1080 \ kg$, The sum of the weight of all boys is: $32 \times 62 = 1984 \ kg$, The sum of the weight of all students is: $1080 + 1984 = 3064 \ kg$, average $= \frac{3064}{50} = 61.28$

24) Choice C is correct

Let x be the original price. If the price of a laptop is decreased by 10% to \$360, then: $90\% \ of \ x = 360 \Rightarrow 0.90x = 360 \Rightarrow x = 360 \div 0.90 = 400$

25) Choice E is correct

Surface Area of a cylinder $= 2\pi r \ (r + h)$, The radius of the cylinder is 8 inches and its height is 12 inches. Surface Area of a cylinder $= 2 \ (\pi) \ (8) \ (8 + 12) = 320 \ \pi$

26) Choice E is correct

$average = \frac{sum \ of \ terms}{number \ of \ terms} \Rightarrow 18 = \frac{13+15+20+x}{4} \Rightarrow 72 = 48 + x \Rightarrow x = 24$

27) Choice C is correct

Let x be the original price. If the price of the sofa is decreased by 25% to \$420, then: $75\% \ of \ x = 420 \Rightarrow 0.75x = 420 \Rightarrow x = 420 \div 0.75 = 560$

28) Choice C is correct

Use simple interest formula: $I = prt$, (I = interest, p = principal, r = rate, t = time)

$I = (8,000)(0.045)(5) = 1,800$

29) Choice E is correct

$(4.2 \times 10^6) \times (2.6 \times 10^{-5}) = (4.2 \times 2.6) \times (10^6 \times 10^{-5}) = 10.92 \times (10^{6 + (-5)})$
$= 1.092 \times 10^2$

30) Choice E is correct

The formula of the volume of pyramid is: $V = \frac{l \times w \times h}{3}$. The length and width of the pyramid is 6 cm and its height is 12 cm. Therefore: $V = \frac{6 \times 6 \times 12}{3} = 144 \ cm^3$

31) Choice E is correct

Simplify:$4(x + 1) = 6(x - 4) + 20, 4x + 4 = 6x - 24 + 20, 4x + 4 = 6x - 4$

Subtract $4x$ from both sides:$4 = 2x - 4$,Add 4 to both sides:$8 = 2x, 4 = x$

32) Choice E is correct

Use distributive property: $2x(4 + 2y) = 8x + 4xy = 4xy + 8x$

33) Choice E is correct

$y = 4ab + 3b^3$, plug in the values of a and b in the equation: $a = 2$ and $b = 3$,

$y = 4(2)(3) + 3(3)^3 = 24 + 3(27) = 24 + 81 = 105$

34) Choice C is correct

$11 \times 36 + 6 \times 12 + 4 = 472$

35) Choice D is correct

Let x be the integer. Then:$2x - 5 = 83$, Add 5 both sides: $2x = 88$, Divide both sides by 2: $x = 44$

36) Choice D is correct

To find the discount, multiply the number by $(100\% - rate\ of\ discount)$.Therefore, for the first discount we get: $(200)(100\% - 15\%) = (200)(0.85)$,For the next 15% discount: $(200)(0.85)(0.85)$.

37) Choice B is correct

Plug in each pair of number in the equation:

A. $(2, 1)$: $2(2) + 4(1) = 8$
B. $(-1, 3)$: $2(-1) + 4(3) = 10$
C. $(-2, 2)$: $2(-2) + 4(2) = 4$
D. $(2, 2)$: $2(2) + 4(2) = 12$

38) Choice B is correct

Use this formula: Percent of Change:$\dfrac{\text{New Value} - \text{Old Value}}{\text{Old Value}} \times 100\%$

$\dfrac{16000 - 20000}{20000} \times 100\% = -20\%$ and $\dfrac{12800 - 16000}{16000} \times 100\% = -20\%$

39) Choice D is correct

The relationship among all sides of special right triangle

$30° - 60° - 90°$ is provided in this triangle:

In this triangle, the opposite side of 30° angle is half of the hypotenuse.

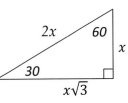
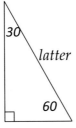
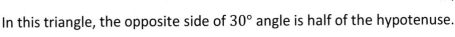

Draw the shape of this question:

The latter is the hypotenuse. Therefore, the latter is $60\ ft$

40) Choice B is correct.

By definition, the sine of any acute angle is equal to the cosine of its complement.

Since, angle A and B are complementary angles, therefore: $\sin A = \cos B$

DAT Quantitative Reasoning Practice Test 2

1) Choice E is correct

$g(x) = -2$, then $f\big(g(x)\big) = f(-2) = 3\,(-2)^3 + 5(-2)^2 + 2(-2) = -24 + 20 - 4 = -8$

2) Choice E is correct

Let x be the width of the rectangle. Use Pythagorean Theorem:

$a^2 + b^2 = c^2$

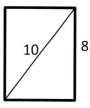

$x^2 + 8^2 = 10^2 \Rightarrow x^2 + 64 = 100 \Rightarrow x^2 = 100 - 64 = 36 \Rightarrow x = 6$

Perimeter of the rectangle = $2\,(length\ +\ width) = 2\,(8 + 6) = 2\,(14) = 28$

3) Choice C is correct

$x = \frac{1}{3}$ and $y = \frac{9}{21}$, substitute the values of x and y in the expression and simplify:

$\frac{1}{x} \div \frac{y}{3} \to \frac{1}{\frac{1}{3}} \div \frac{\frac{9}{21}}{3} \to \frac{1}{\frac{1}{3}} = 3$ and $\frac{\frac{9}{21}}{3} = \frac{9}{63} = \frac{1}{7}$. Then: $\frac{1}{\frac{1}{3}} \div \frac{\frac{9}{21}}{3} = 3 \div \frac{1}{7} = 3 \times 7 = 21$

4) Choice A is correct

$average\ (mean) = \frac{sum\ of\ terms}{number\ of\ terms} \Rightarrow 85 = \frac{sum\ of\ terms}{50} \Rightarrow sum = 85 \times 50 = 4250$

The difference of 94 and 69 is 25. Therefore, 25 should be subtracted from the sum.

$4250 - 25 = 4225,\ mean = \frac{sum\ of\ terms}{number\ of\ terms} \Rightarrow mean = \frac{4225}{50} = 84.5$

5) Choice D is correct

Solve for x. $x - 4 \le 4x - 8 < 16 \Rightarrow$ (add 8 all sides) $-4 + 8 < 4x - 8 + 8 < 16 + 8 \Rightarrow$

$4 < 4x < 24 \Rightarrow$ (divide all sides by 4) $1 \le x < 6$. x is between 1 and 6. Choice D represents this inequality.

6) Choice E is correct

Use formula of rectangle prism volume.

$$V = (length)(width)(height) \Rightarrow 2000 = (25)(10)(height) \Rightarrow height$$
$$= 2000 \div 250 = 8$$

7) Choice C is correct

To find the number of possible outfit combinations, multiply number of options for each factor:

$3 \times 7 \times 4 = 84$

8) Choice B is correct

The diagonal of the square is 8. Let x be the side. Use Pythagorean Theorem: $a^2 + b^2 = c^2$

$x^2 + x^2 = 8^2 \Rightarrow 2x^2 = 8^2 \Rightarrow 2x^2 = 64 \Rightarrow x^2 = 32 \Rightarrow x = \sqrt{32}$

The area of the square is: $\sqrt{32} \times \sqrt{32} = 32$

9) Choice A is correct

The width of the rectangle is twice its length. Let x be the length. Then, $width = 2x$

Perimeter of the rectangle is $2(width + length) = 2(2x + x) = 60 \Rightarrow 6x = 60 \Rightarrow x = 10$

Length of the rectangle is 10 meters.

10) Choice D is correct

$average = \dfrac{sum\ of\ terms}{number\ of\ terms} \Rightarrow$ (average of 6 numbers) $12 = \dfrac{sum\ of\ numbers}{6} \Rightarrow$ sum of 6 numbers is $12 \times 6 = 72,$

(average of 4 numbers) $10 = \dfrac{sum\ of\ numbers}{4} \Rightarrow$ sum of 4 numbers is $10 \times 4 = 40$

$sum\ of\ 6\ numbers - sum\ of\ 4\ numbers = sum\ of\ 2\ numbers$

$72 - 40 = 32$, average of 2 numbers $= \dfrac{32}{2} = 16$

11) Choice C is correct

Solve for the sum of five numbers.

$average = \dfrac{sum\ of\ terms}{number\ of\ terms} \Rightarrow 24 = \dfrac{sum\ of\ 5\ numbers}{5} \Rightarrow$ sum of 5 numbers $= 24 \times 5 = 120$

The sum of 5 numbers is 120. If a sixth number 42 is added, then the sum of 6 numbers is

$$120 + 42 = 162, \; average = \frac{\text{sum of terms}}{\text{number of terms}} = \frac{162}{6} = 27$$

12) Choice D is correct

Th ratio of boy to girls is $4 : 7$. Therefore, there are 4 boys out of 11 students. To find the answer, first divide the total number of students by 11, then multiply the result by 4.

$66 \div 11 = 6 \Rightarrow 6 \times 4 = 24$, There are 24 boys and 42 $(66 - 24)$ girls. So, 18 more boys should be enrolled to make the ratio $1 : 1$.

13) Choice D is correct

Jason needs an 76% average to pass for five exams. Therefore, the sum of 5 exams must be at lease $5 \times 76 = 380$, The sum of 4 exams is: $68 + 72 + 85 + 90 = 315$.

The minimum score Jason can earn on his fifth and final test to pass is:$380 - 315 = 65$

14) Choice A is correct
Let x be the integer. Then: $2x - 5 = 53$. Add 5 both sides: $2x = 58$, Divide both sides by 2:

$\quad x = 29$

15) Choice B is correct

Use simple interest formula:$I = prt$,(I = interest, p = principal, r = rate, t = time)

$I = (12000)(0.035)(2) = 840$

16) Choice D is correct

Simplify. $6x^2y^3(2x^2y)^3 = 6x^2y^3(8x^6y^3) = 48x^8y^6$

17) Choice C is correct

Surface Area of a cylinder $= 2\pi r(r + h)$, The radius of the cylinder is 6 inches and its height is 12 inches. π is about 3.14. Then: Surface Area of a cylinder $= 2(\pi)(6)(6 + 12) = 216\,\pi = 678.24$

18) Choice E is correct

$\quad$ Use Pythagorean Theorem: $a^2 + b^2 = c^2$

$80^2 + 150^2 = c^2 \Rightarrow 6400 + 22500 = c^2 \Rightarrow 28900 = c^2 \Rightarrow c = 170$

19) Choice E is correct

Plug in 104 for F and then solve for C.

$$C = \frac{5}{9}(F - 32) \Rightarrow C = \frac{5}{9}(140 - 32) \Rightarrow C = \frac{5}{9}(108) = 60$$

20) Choice A is correct

First, find the number. Let x be the number. Write the equation and solve for x.

150% of a number is 75, then: $1.5 \times x = 75 \Rightarrow x = 75 \div 1.5 = 50$

95% of 50 is: $0.95 \times 50 = 47.5$

21) Choice C is correct

the population is increased by 15% and 20%. 15% increase changes the population to 115% of original population. For the second increase, multiply the result by 120%.

$(1.15) \times (1.20) = 1.38 = 138\%$.38 percent of the population is increased after two years.

22) Choice C is correct

Three times of 24,000 is 72,000. One sixth of them cancelled their tickets. One sixth of 72,000 equals 12,000 ($\frac{1}{6} \times 72000 = 12000$). 60,000 $(72000 - 12000 = 60000)$ fans are attending this week.

23) Choice E is correct

The area of the square is 64 inches. Therefore, the side of the square is square root of the area. $\sqrt{64} = 8$ inches. Four times the side of the square is the perimeter: $4 \times 8 = 32 \; inches$

24) Choice D is correct

The equation of a line is in the form of $y = mx + b$, where m is the slope of the line and b is the $y - intercept$ of the line. Two points (4,3) and (3,2) are on line A. Therefore, the slope of the line A is: $slope \; of \; line \; A = \frac{y_2 - y_1}{x_2 - x_1} = \frac{2-3}{3-4} = \frac{-1}{-1} = 1$

The slope of line A is 1. Thus, the formula of the line A is: $y = mx + b = x + b$, choose a point and plug in the values of x and y in the equation to solve for b. Let's choose point (4, 3). Then:

$y = x + b \rightarrow 3 = 4 + b \rightarrow b = 3 - 4 = -1$

The equation of line A is: $y = x - 1$

Now, let's review the choices provided:

A. $(-1, 2)$ $\quad\quad\quad$ $y = x - 1 \rightarrow 2 = -1 - 1 = -2$ $\quad$ This is not true.

B. $(5, 7)$ $\quad\quad\quad$ $y = x - 1 \rightarrow 7 = 5 - 1 = 4$ $\quad\quad$ This is not true.

C. $(3, 4)$ $\quad\quad\quad$ $y = x - 1 \rightarrow 4 = 3 - 1 = 2$ $\quad\quad$ This is not true.

D. $(-1, -2)$ $\quad\quad$ $y = x - 1 \rightarrow -2 = -1 - 1 = -2$ $\quad$ This is true!

E. $(-7, -9)$ $\qquad\qquad y = x - 1 \to -9 = -7 - 1 = -8$ This is not true!

25) Choice E is correct

$g(x) = -2$, then $f\big(g(x)\big) = f(-2) = 2\,(-2)^3 + 5(-2)^2 + 2(-2) = -16 + 20 - 4 = 0$

26) Choice E is correct

The formula for the area of the circle is: $A = \pi r^2$.**The area is** 64π. **Therefore:** $A = \pi r^2 \Rightarrow 64\pi = \pi r^2$

Divide both sides by π:$64 = r^2 \Rightarrow r = 8$. Diameter of a circle is $2 \times$ radius. Then:

Diameter $= 2 \times 8 = 16$

27) Choice C is correct

Write a proportion and solve for x.$\frac{3}{2} = \frac{x}{22} \Rightarrow 2x = 3 \times 22 \Rightarrow x = 33\,ft$

28) Choice A is correct

Use FOIL method. $(4x + 2y)(2x - y) = 8x^2 - 4xy + 4xy - 2y^2 = 8x^2 - 2y^2$

29) Choice D is correct

To solve absolute values equations, write two equations. $x - 10$ could be positive 3, or negative 3. Therefore, $x - 10 = 3 \Rightarrow x = 13$,$x - 10 = -3 \Rightarrow x = 7$, Find the product of solutions: $7 \times 13 = 91$

30) Choice B is correct

The equation of a line in slope intercept form is: $y = mx + b$. Solve for y. $4x - 2y = 8 \Rightarrow -2y = 8 - 4x \Rightarrow y = (8 - 4x) \div (-2) \Rightarrow y = 2x - 4$. The slope is 2. The slope of the line perpendicular to this line is: $m_1 \times m_2 = -1 \Rightarrow 2 \times m_2 = -1 \Rightarrow m_2 = -\frac{1}{2}$

31) Choice C is correct

Plug in the value of x and y. $x = 3$ and $y = -2$,

$5(x - 2y) + (2 - x)^2 = 5(3 - 2(-2)) + (2 - 3)^2 = 5(3 + 4) + (-1)^2 = 35 + 1 = 36$

32) Choice E is correct

The distance between Jason and Joe is 15 miles. Jason running at 5.5 miles per hour and Joe is running at the speed of 7 miles per hour. Therefore, every hour the distance is 1.5 miles less.

$15 \div 1.5 = 10$

33) Choice D is correct

The failing rate is 11 out of $88 = \frac{11}{88}$, Change the fraction to percent: $\frac{11}{88} \times 100\% = 12.5\%$

12.5 percent of students failed. Therefore, 87.5 percent of students passed the exam.

34) Choice B is correct

$$tan\theta = \frac{opposite}{adjacent}$$

$tan\theta = \frac{5}{12} \Rightarrow$ we have the following right triangle. Then:

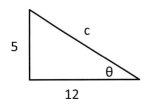

$$c = \sqrt{5^2 + 12^2} = \sqrt{25 + 144} = \sqrt{169} = 13$$

$$cos\theta = \frac{adjacent}{hypotenuse} = \frac{12}{13}$$

35) Choice B is correct

The area of trapezoid is: $\left(\frac{8+12}{2}\right) \times x = 100 \rightarrow 10x = 100 \rightarrow x = 10$

$$y = \sqrt{3^2 + 4^2} = 5$$

Perimeter is: $12 + 10 + 8 + 5 = 35$

36) Choice C is correct

Set of number that are not composite between 1 and 25: $A = \{1, 2, 3, 5, 7, 11, 13, 17, 19, 23\}$

$$\text{Probability} = \frac{number\ of\ desired\ outcomes}{number\ of\ total\ outcomes} = \frac{10}{25} = \frac{2}{5}$$

37) Choice D is correct

Check each choice provided:

A. 1 $\frac{4+5+8+11+12}{5} = \frac{40}{5} = 8$

B. 4 $\frac{1+5+8+11+12}{5} = \frac{37}{5} = 7.4$

C. 5 $\frac{1+4+8+11+12}{5} = \frac{36}{5} = 7.2$

D. 11 $\frac{1+4+5+8+12}{5} = \frac{30}{5} = 6$

E. 12 $\frac{1+4+5+8+11}{5} = \frac{29}{5} = 5.8$

38) Choice A is correct

$sinA = \frac{1}{3} \Rightarrow$

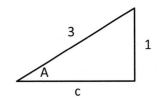

Since $\sin\theta = \frac{opposite}{hypotenuse}$, we have the following right triangle. Then:

$$c = \sqrt{3^2 - 1^2} = \sqrt{9 - 1} = \sqrt{8}$$

$$cosA = \frac{\sqrt{8}}{3}$$

39) Choice C is correct

Plug in the value of each choice in the inequality.

A.	1	$(1-2)^2 + 1 > 3(1) - 1 \rightarrow 2 > 2$	No!
B.	6	$(6-2)^2 + 1 > 3(6) - 1 \rightarrow 17 > 17$	No!
C.	8	$(8-2)^2 + 1 > 3(8) - 1 \rightarrow 37 > 23$	Bingo!
D.	3	$(3-2)^2 + 1 > 3(3) - 1 \rightarrow 2 > 8$	No!
E.	4	$(4-2)^2 + 1 > 3(4) - 1 \rightarrow 5 > 11$	No!

40) Choice A is correct.

The relationship among all sides of right triangle $30° - 60° - 90°$ is provided in the following triangle: Sine of $30°$ equals to: $\frac{opposite}{hypotenuse} = \frac{x}{2x} = \frac{1}{2}$

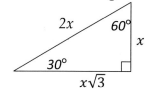

"Effortless Math Education" Publications

Effortless Math authors' team strives to prepare and publish the best quality DAT Quantitative Reasoning learning resources to make learning Math easier for all. We hope that our publications help you learn Math in an effective way and prepare for the DAT test.

We all in Effortless Math wish you good luck and successful studies!

Effortless Math Authors

www.EffortlessMath.com

... So Much More Online!

✓ FREE Math lessons

✓ More Math learning books!

✓ Mathematics Worksheets

✓ Online Math Tutors

Need a PDF version of this book?

Visit www.EffortlessMath.com

Made in United States
North Haven, CT
29 August 2022